G000069612

BIOCHEMISTRY RESEARCH TRENDS

ADVANCES IN LIPOSOMES RESEARCH

BIOCHEMISTRY RESEARCH TRENDS

Additional books in this series can be found on Nova's website under the Series tab.

Additional e-books in this series can be found on Nova's website under the e-book tab.

BIOCHEMISTRY RESEARCH TRENDS

ADVANCES IN LIPOSOMES RESEARCH

LAUREN FINNEY
EDITOR

New York

Library of Congress Cataloging-in-Publication Data

ISBN: 978-1-63117-074-4

Library of Congress Control Number: 2014930027

Published by Nova Science Publishers, Inc. † New York

CONTENTS

PREFACE

In this book the authors present current research in the study of liposomes. Topics discusses in this compilation include liposome mediated malaria vaccine development; liposomal delivery of antimicrobial agents in advances in liposome research; trends on microfluidic liposome production through hydrodynamic flow-focusing and microdroplet techniques for gene delivery applications; liposomes as important drug carriers in cancer therapy; liposome application in the veterinary field; and design of liposomes with a pH-sensitive fluorescent dye and gramicidin channels for immune-sensing.

Chapter 1 - The introduction of vaccine technology has facilitated an unprecedented multi-antigen approach to develop an effective vaccine against complex systemic inflammatory human malaria (*Plasmodium falciparum*). The capacity of multi subunit DNA vaccine encoding different stage Plasmodium antigens to induce $CD8^+$ cytotoxic T lymphocytes and interferon-responses in mice, monkeys and humans has been observed. The cytotoxic T cell responses are categorically needed against intracellular hepatic stage and humoral response with antibodies targeted against antigens from all stages of malaria parasite life cycle. As genetic vaccination is capable of eliciting both cell mediated and humoral immune responses, the key to success for any DNA vaccine is to design a vector able to serve as a safe and efficient delivery system. This has encouraged development of non-viral DNA-mediated gene transfer techniques such as liposome, virosomes, microsphere and nanoparticles. The efficient and relatively safe DNA transfection using lipoplexes makes them an appealing alternative for gene delivery. In addition, liposome entrapped DNA has been shown to enhance the potency of DNA vaccines, possibly by facilitating uptake of the plasmid by antigen-presenting cells (APC). The control of residual non-adaptive immune effecters (mainly wandering macrophages and polymorphonuclears) by clodronate-loaded liposome in NSG immunodeficient mice further advocates their value for translational biomedical research.

Chapter 2 - Chronic and slow/non-healing wounds require extensive management to reduce the repair and recovery time. Wound dressings and devices are often designed to suit varying wound characteristics and strategically manage the complexity of different wound types. The main challenges in managing the chronic wound environment include:

- delivery of sufficient antimicrobial agent to maintain bioavailability at biocidal concentrations
- control of the quantity of wound exudate whilst promoting/ maintaining the availability of pro-healing factors
- reduction of the risk of uneven antimicrobial deposition, lowering the risk of localized toxicity
- improvement in the ease of antimicrobial and wound dressing application
- reduction of the frequency of dressing changes thus minimising patient discomfort and avoid risk opportunity for further infection

Topical administration of agents can require penetration through dead matter, purulent exudates and scar tissue as well as the dermis, which serves as the first line of defence. The dermal barrier has low permeability to large hydrophilic entities but will selectively allow permeation of small lipophilic molecules. Whilst essential for maintenance of host homeostasis, this limited permeability dramatically restricts delivery of many antimicrobial agents both to the wound surface as well as into the various layers of the dermis. These issues can be reduced with the aid of controlled release drug delivery systems such as liposomes, which can improve targeting, efficacy and the biopharmaceutical properties of the antimicrobial agent. Liposomes are biocompatible, biodegradable, lipid bilayer vesicles with a large aqueous inner-core for encapsulation and delivery of active agents. Encapsulation of antimicrobial agents in liposomes provides protection from enzymatic and immunological inactivation. Additionally, the liposome's capacity to bind water may aid moisture retention, which promotes an environment that is highly conducive to tissue repair. The capacity to transport both hydrophilic and hydrophobic materials, has allowed a wide range of pharmaceutical formulations to be incorporated into liposome vesicles. In terms of encapsulation, agents with varying lipophilicities can be sequestered within the phospholipid bilayer (hydrophobic), entrapped in the inner core (hydrophilic), as well as in the inner and outer bilayer interface (hydrophilic) of the liposome. This ability of liposomes to encapsulate antimicrobial agents with a broad range of physicochemical properties makes them valuable in wound management applications. This chapter will examine the diverse antimicrobial payloads, including antibiotics, antifungals, natural products and essential oils, which are amenable to liposome delivery and show enhanced therapeutic outcomes. The advantages of liposome encapsulated antimicrobials are their potential to achieve effective drug delivery whilst reducing problems related to targeting, biodistribution and bioavailability of microbiocidal agents.

Chapter 3 – Recent studies on liposome production for gene delivery have aimed to obtain final formulations with physicochemical properties, like size and polydispersity in optimum ranges for biological applications without the need for post-processing steps. In this context, microfluidics emerges as a promising technology to overcome the major challenges of the pharmaceutical industry, especially for gene delivery purposes. In this field, microfluidic hydrodynamic focusing (MHF) technique and microfluidic based in droplets were used for liposomes production and to complex liposomes with nucleic acids. Essentially, MHF technique is composed by a central organic stream of lipids dispersed in alcohol hydrodynamically focused by two adjacent aqueous streams; the water-alcohol diffusion along the main microchannel forms instability regions for the phospholipids that self-assemble into vesicles. Additionally, MHF technique allows the formation of monodisperse nanosized liposomes in one-step for a variety of applications. The other technique, microfluidic based in droplets, was described as an innovative and promising technique. Basically, the droplet contains the aqueous phase with liposome and nucleic acid and it is stabilized in the oil phase by a surface active compound. The main advantage of microdroplet platform is to allow more rapid mixing, generating complex with smaller size and polydispersity, forming the aggregates inside microsized droplets in emulsions. Thus, in this chapter, we summarize recent studies and trends on microfluidics liposomes context about liposomes in the microfluidic techniques context, for production of liposomes through the MHF and microfluidic droplet techniques emphasizing future applications in the gene delivery field. We hope that the main findings of the state-of-the-art disclosed herein can be useful for rational use of microfluidics devices for liposome production for formation of nonviral gene delivery systems.

Chapter 4 – Normal human cells grow, multiply and die, by it self control process. When there is loss of this cell control it start a fast and reproducible division that may lead to the invasion to other normal cells and tissues. This uncontrolled growth and aggressive process, in most of the cases, featuring a set of more than 100 different types of diseases called normally as cancer. Among the forms of treatment for cancer in general, chemotherapy, radiotherapy and surgery are the most acceptable and used, (alone or combined), however, early diagnosis is essential for effective healing or eradication of the diseases. These treatments do not affect only the damaged tissue and cause undesirable side effects such as hair loss, nausea and other, increased risk of infections, asthenia, intestinal obstruction and even mutilation once in some cases surgery compromise patient life, may lead to irreversible psychological damage. Therefore there is a need for new therapeutic methods that enable reduction of the tumor and restricting adverse effects to diseased tissue while protecting the healthy tissue. These could be archive by the use of specific drugs in the conventional treatments as well as with new therapeutic approaches whose goal is to reducing the tumor size and spread process and with protocol minimally invasive with restriction of adverse effects in the diseased tissue what is essential for achieving a successful outcome. Liposomes as Drug delivery system have been studied over the last 3 decades as DDS with special appeal when applied to anti-cancer therapy and to treat many other diseases. Standing out among the nanosized systems for drug delivery because they allow the incorporation of hydrophobic drugs in the lipid bilayer and hydrophilic drugs in the aqueous phase, while maintaining their physical and chemical characteristics, as well as promoting their selective distribution in tissues when incorporated efficiently to liposomes. This selective distribution in tissues is greater in the case of cancer cells, since these have high metabolism and require higher nutrient. This chapter provides a general approach with the discussion of the liposome research focusing in cancer treatment and the introduction of two new liposomal system applied in combination with a an alternative protocol know as photodynamic therapy (PDT), one of them containing cisplatin - conventional chemotherapeutic - for synergistic effect with the chloro-aluminum phthalocyanine and other containing folic acid vetorizador of the drug to treat mamarin and other visceral cancers.

Chapter 5 – In the field of veterinary medicine, liposomes are the most widespread nanotechnological tool. Already for some time, they have been applied in animal therapies to improve delivery of different drugs, comprising analgesic, antiviral, antimicrobial, antifungal, and anticancer agents. More recently, with the rise of recombinant DNA technologies, liposomes have been included in veterinary vaccine formulations to entrap antigen-coding DNAs, siRNAs, peptides, and recombinant antigens, as well as effectors of the innate immune system, in order to elicit protective responses against viruses, bacteria and parasites. Reported applications include their use in companion and productive animals, among others horse, dog, cattle, poultry, and fish. Liposomes are generally well tolerated and, in accordance with their purpose, may be delivered through the intramuscular, subcutaneous, intravenous, ocular, and/or intranasal route to their desired target. In order to achieve a more specific tissue targeting, engineering of liposomes has also been described in the veterinary field. Besides therapeutics, liposomes have also been applied in transfection technologies and in the cryopreservation of stallion or bull semen. Use of liposomes can be limited by the high manufacturing costs of lipid synthesis or purification. Therefore, the formulation of low-cost liposomes made of non-purified lipid mixtures will open the possibility of large-scale applications in animal productive systems. This chapter presents an overview on possibilities, advantages, and perspectives of liposome employment for veterinary use.

Chapter 6 - In this review, the authors describe a liposome array for direct fluorometric immunoassay using liposomes encapsulating a pH-sensitive fluorescent dye, BCECF ([2',7'-bis(carboxyethyl)-4 or 5-carboxyfluorescein]). The method has a signal amplification system based on modulation of channel kinetics of gramicidin, which forms a nanopore in a lipid bilayer and allows permeating monovalent cations. The detection of analytes is performed without any lysis of liposomes and labeling with a fluorescent molecule. Instead, immunoreactions between analyte and $F_{ab'}$ fragment linked to liposomes are monitored though a fluorescence change of the encapsulated dye, which depends on the channel activity of gramicidin. The assay is simple, rapid and highly sensitive. The method allowed quantification of substance P (SP), neurokinin A, growth-hormone-related peptides, and streptolysin O (SLO) at sub-pg to ng level. The highly sensitive assay was applied to detection of SP and SLO in human serum by simply diluting the sample 125 times (0.8% human serum). The method has the potential of applying it as a bioanalytical technique for clinical analyses and diagnoses.

In: Advances in Liposomes Research
Editor: Lauren Finney

ISBN: 978-1-63117-074-4

Chapter 1

LIPOSOME-MEDIATED MALARIA VACCINE DEVELOPMENT: MORE THAN A TOUR DE FORCE

Rajeev K. Tyagi[1, 2*], Neeraj K. Garg[3] and Tejram Sahu[4]

[1]Department of Periodontics, College of Dental Medicine, Georgia Regents University, Augusta, GA, US

[2]Malaria Vaccine Development Laboratory, Institute Pasteur, Paris, France

[3] Drug Delivery Research Group, University Institute of Pharmaceutical Sciences, Panjab University, Chandigarh, India

[4]National Institute of Allergy and Infectious Diseases, Rockville, MD, US

ABSTRACT

The introduction of vaccine technology has facilitated an unprecedented multi-antigen approach to develop an effective vaccine against complex systemic inflammatory human malaria (*Plasmodium falciparum*). The capacity of multi subunit DNA vaccine encoding different stage Plasmodium antigens to induce $CD8^+$ cytotoxic T

---

* Corresponding Author: Rajeev K. Tyagi, M. Sc, Ph. D. Department of Periodontics, College of Dental Medicine, Georgia Regents University, 1120 15th Street, CB 2716, Augusta, Georgia 30912, USA. Tel: 1-706-721-8622; Fax: 1-706-723-0215; Email: rtyagi@gru.edu

lymphocytes and interferon-responses in mice, monkeys and humans has been observed. The cytotoxic T cell responses are categorically needed against intracellular hepatic stage and humoral response with antibodies targeted against antigens from all stages of malaria parasite life cycle. As genetic vaccination is capable of eliciting both cell mediated and humoral immune responses, the key to success for any DNA vaccine is to design a vector able to serve as a safe and efficient delivery system. This has encouraged development of non-viral DNA-mediated gene transfer techniques such as liposome, virosomes, microsphere and nanoparticles. The efficient and relatively safe DNA transfection using lipoplexes makes them an appealing alternative for gene delivery. In addition, liposome entrapped DNA has been shown to enhance the potency of DNA vaccines, possibly by facilitating uptake of the plasmid by antigen-presenting cells (APC). The control of residual non-adaptive immune effecters (mainly wandering macrophages and polymorphonuclears) by clodronate-loaded liposome in NSG immunodeficient mice further advocates their value for translational biomedical research.

1. Background: The Burden of Malaria

Malaria continues to present a major health challenge in many of the poor countries in the world, with 225 million cases leading to an estimated 781,000 deaths in 2009 [1]. Numerous efforts towards control and eradication of this disease are directed at different areas including insect vector control, vaccine development, and the discovery of new therapeutic drugs. Although, battle to control malaria has been fought on several grounds including improved methodologies of diagnosis and chemo prophylaxisas well as integrated vector control through various physical methods such as treatment with insecticide and house spraying [2], prevalence and resurgence of malaria continues to persist because of drug resistant parasites and insecticide resistant vector [3, 4]. Therefore, due to this bleak situation, the need to develop additional control measures such as malaria vaccine is both attractive and urgent. The malaria vaccine is still elusive despite of enormous and continued efforts on to develop an effective vaccine [5]

There are number of existing approaches to malaria vaccine based on attenuated sporozoite, synthetic and recombinant immunogenic peptides. These strategies have proved significant in terms of safety, duration of immunity and specificity [6-10]. As vaccines based on live, attenuated malaria parasites, are economically and technically not feasible, malaria research focuses on recombinant or synthetic subunit vaccines. The optimal vaccine should have the ability to elicit protective immunity blocking infection, prevents pathology and blocks transmission of parasite. Therefore, combination vaccine consisting subunits from different stage of the parasite would meet all these requirements. The progress in developing a malaria vaccine is not going up to that pace as it was expected after the complete genome sequencing of *P. falciparum* [11], perhaps, in part because of the larger genetic diversity of *plasmodium* parasite. Thus identification, expression and degree of variability of candidate vaccine antigens render it more complex to understand various biological processes of parasite. The complex life cycle of malaria parasite and antigenic diversity are the barriers associated with vaccine development [12].

2. Biology of Malaria Parasite: Approaches for Effective Immune Interventions

The causative agent of malaria parasite has a complex multi-stage life cycle involving both primary (mosquito) and secondary (human) hosts in different cellular environments (intra and extracellular) in which the parasite develops. The disease in humans is caused by one or a combination of four species of Plasmodia: *P. vivax, P. falciparum, P.malariae,* and *P. ovale.* Also, in geographically limited zones of South-East Asia, the Malaysian island of Borneo in particular, infections by *P. knowlesi* as a zoonose have been known to occur [13-15]. While it remains a possibility, there does not appear to be any evidence to indicate that infections of this "fifth human malaria parasite" can be transmitted from humans to other human hosts [16] and hence they are not considered to be important in terms of public health outside these zones. Malaria parasite has a large genome of 14 chromosomes comprising 26-30 mega bases encoding around 5000-6000 proteins [17, 18]. Most of the *Plasmodium* strains have a complex life cycle that begins when a female mosquito injects sporozoites into the skin of an individual at the time of blood meal. After differentiation and passing through various forms, parasite produces thousands of merozoites that are released from the hepatocytes and rapidly invade circulating erythrocytes. The rupture of infected erythrocytes in the blood circulation release pigments initiating malaria related symptoms (Figure 1).

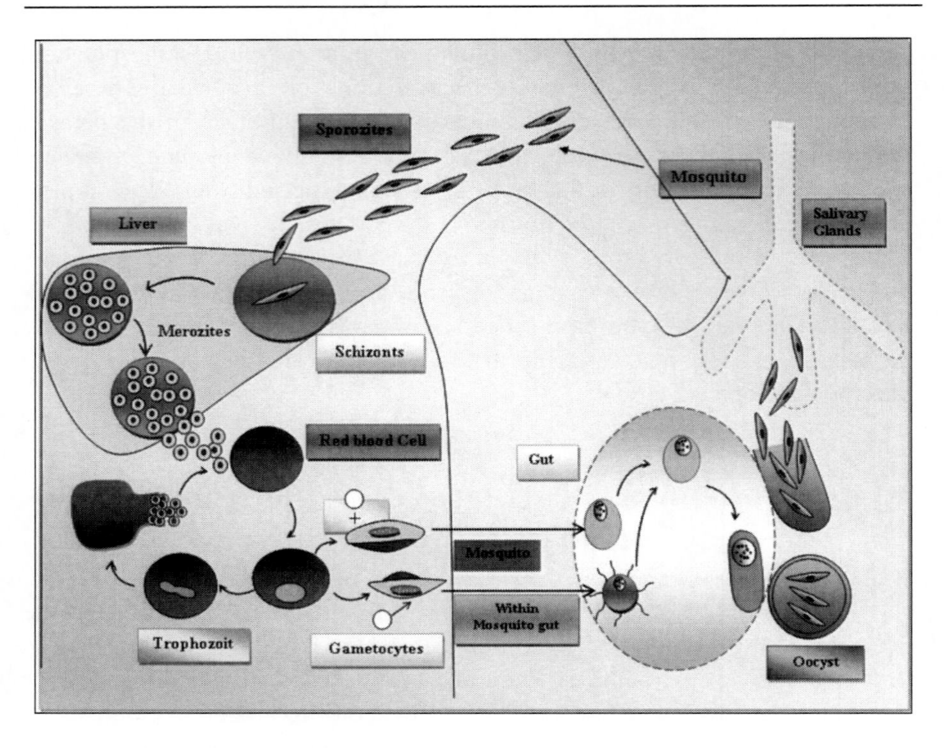

Figure 1. Life cycle of malaria parasite.

3. Existing Malaria Vaccines

Although the complexity and genome variability of the parasite hampers the development of a universal, effective and long lasting vaccine, the feasibility of malaria vaccine is supported by the several lines of evidence. The repeated exposure of malaria develops natural immunity against un-wanted clinical manifestations of infection [19]. In addition, passive transfer of antibodies and immune effectors from an immunized animal to the susceptible host induces protection against malaria infection [20].

3.1. Pre-Erythrocytic Vaccines

The pre-erythrocytic vaccine is aimed to prevent the entry of sporozoites into the hepatocytes and their development into tissue schizonts. The clinical manifestation of the disease and further transmission of Plasmodia to mosquito may be prevented by completely blocking this phase of the cycle, thereby making this vaccine efficient [19]. Furthermore, protection of humans from malaria infection by vaccination targeting the pre-erythrocytic stages has been experimentally verified by exposing the volunteers to 200-1000 infective bites by irradiated mosquito and volunteers were further challenged with mosquitoes harboring the *P. vivax* and *P. falciparum* infectious sporozoites. The significant protection was observed in the patients immunized with more than 100 bites from infected and irradiated sporozoite infective challenge [21, 22]. These vaccines aim to protect against malaria infection and ideally should provide sterilizing humoral immunity by eliciting antibodies that target the invading sporozoites and prevent them from invading the liver.

3.1.1. DNA Vaccines and Live Recombinant Vaccines

Certain vaccines based on the CSP antigen include plasmid DNA vaccines and live recombinant vaccines that use the attenuated modified vaccinia Ankara (MVA) strain, fowl poxvirus (FPV), Adenovirus, Sind-bis virus, yellow fever virus or a cold-adapted attenuated influenza virus strain as a vector, and some of these vaccines have been tested together in prime boost combinations [23, 24].

A multiple-antigen DNA vaccine (MuStDO-5) has been designed to encode five different liver-stage antigens: CSP, liver stage antigens 1 and 3 (LSA-1 and -3), exported protein 1 (EXP1), and the sporozoite surface protein 2 (SSP2, also known as thrombospondinrelated adhesive protein, TRAP). MuStDo-5 was manufactured as a combination of five separate plasmids and vaccine (administered with GM-CSF DNA as an adjuvant), was safe and well tolerated in mice and rabbits [25], but showed weak immunogenicity in primates and no evidence of protection was obtained in Phase IIa challenge trials [26-28].

Expression of liver-stage antigen 1 (LSA-1) begins within the infected hepatocyte and several studies have shown association between LSA-1 specific immune responses and protection from severe disease or parasitaemia [29]. The lack of a known homologue in species of malaria that infect mice or non-human primates has retarded vaccine development. Liver-stage antigen 3 (LSA-3) is less characterized than CS, TRAP or LSA-1. A vaccination study, however, showed protection using lipopeptide and recombinant protein LSA-3 constructs, but the expression of this antigen by blood-stage parasites complicates interpretation of results [30, 31].

3.2. Asexual Blood Stage Vaccines/Erythrocytic Stage Vaccine

These vaccines are aimed primarily for the protection against severe malaria. The inhibition of parasite invasion cycles will lead to reduced parasite burden and decreased morbidity and mortality. The blood stage vaccine candidates currently lack a human artificial challenge model (mouse- human chimera) and have to rely on natural challenge in field trials unlike pre-erythrocytic vaccine candidates.

The antigens responsible for invasion of the red cell have been targeted for the formulation of blood stage vaccine. The well-known and characterized antigen is MSP-1, the major surface protein of merozoites. The antibodies against C-terminus of MSP-1 are associated with protection from high parasitaemia [32]. Additionally, these vaccines have been shown to inhibit parasite growth *in vitro* [33] and prevent red cell invasion [34]. These antibodies probably inhibit parasite entry by preventing a proteolytic cleavage of MSP-1 protein to a smaller fragment essential for successful invasion [35].

3.3. Transmission Blocking Vaccines (Sexual Stage Vaccines)

The sporogonic phase of the cycle is initiated by fertilization of the gametocyte in mosquito midgut, which further develops to produce an abundant number of sporozoites injected again into the vertebrate host. It has been shown that both antibodies and likely cytokines are capable of blocking the fertilization process and parasite development in mosquito [36].These vaccines are aimed to induce antibodies against the sexual stage antigens in order to prevent development of infectious sporozoites in salivary glands of Anopheles mosquitoes [37]. The leading vaccine candidates contain *P. falciparum* ookinete surface antigens Pfs25 and Pfs28 or their *P. vivax* homologues Pvs25 and Pvs28 [38]. The other sexual stage-specific antigens that have been employed to develop transmission-blocking vaccine(s), are Pfs48/45 and Pfs230 [39].

In essence, despite various impediments such as lack of sufficient immune response and enough protection against disease, recombinant DNA technology has its real advantages over the conventional approaches to vaccination as they express antigen over a prolonged period of time.

4. DNA Vaccine and Problems Associated with the Naked Plasmid DNA Vaccine

The observation that w/o/w emulsion, or incorporation of monophosphoryl lipid A or QS 21 could augment the response significantly underscore the need to find presentation and delivery methods. An emulsion is defined as a dispersion of a liquid called the dispersed phase in a second liquid termed continuous phase with which the first one is not miscible. In vaccine formulations, these phases are water (antigenic media) and oil. The surfactants are added in order to stabilize the emulsion. A surfactant is a compound containing a polar group (hydrophilic) and a non-polar group (hydrophobic) and often composed of a fatty acid chain. Presently, no universal adjuvant available therefore emulsions may prove to be good adjuvant systems like monophosphoryl lipid A [40, 41] which increases the function of antigen-presenting cells and open new ways for developing delivery methods. In case of malaria parasites CTL response is categorically needed against intracellular hepatic stage while humoral response with antibodies targeted against antigens from all stages of life cycle. This necessitates a multivalent DNA vaccine encoding various stage antigens to evoke $CD8^+$ CTL response and humoral responses to block/ prevent infection or transmission.

The effective immunization using naked DNA (generally administered intramuscularly) suffers various bio-barriers and impediments. The uptake of DNA by myocytes is low and therefore it necessitates larger dose administration often into regenerating muscles. It is also likely that some of the injected DNA suffers deoxyribonuclease attack [42]. Although myocytes carry MHC-I molecules, they are not professional antigen presenting cells (APC) due to insufficient vital co-stimulatory molecules. It is thought that responses to genetic vaccines are, at least in part, the result of transfer of antigenic material from myocytes to professional APC.

5. Advantages of Liposome(s) as an Antigen Carrier in Vaccine Development

Liposomes are vesicles of varying size consisting of a spherical lipid bilayer and an aqueous inner compartment that are generated *in vitro*. The distinct advantage of liposomes is their ability to encapsulate various materials combined with their structural flexibility and versatility. Predominance in drug delivery and targeting has enabled liposomes to be used as therapeutic tool in tumor targeting, gene silencing, anti-sense therapy, immunomodulation and most importantly genetic vaccination [43, 44].

Liposome has been used for the targeted and controlled delivery of macromolecules like proteins, peptides, antigens and plasmid construct of DNA. These have proved valuable tools in terms of powerful Th1 adjuvant system for the production of potent cellular responses with mycobacterial lipid [45]. Liposome (pH sensitive liposome) mediates cytosolic delivery of macromolecules, and its possible role in vaccine development has been documented [46]. The direct cytosolic delivery of carboxyl-terminal 19 kDa fragment of merozoite surface protein-1 of *Plasmodium falciparum* (PfMSP-1_{19}) through pH sensitive liposome have shown to enhance immunogenicity [47]. The gel-cored liposome (Engineered liposome) has been used to overcome low immunogenicity, and to prolong release of entrapped content. A core of polymer was incorporated inside liposomal vesicles that act as a cytoskeleton providing mechanical strength to vesicles. Thus, BSA loaded gel core liposomes were prepared by reverse phase evaporation method and characterized for vesicles size, shape, entrapment efficiency, *in vitro* release and stability studies justifying its potential for improved vaccine delivery [48]. The potential utility of novel carrier gel core liposomes for intramuscular delivery of transmission blocking antigen Pfs25 has been investigated. In addition, this study evaluated an effect of co-administration of vaccine adjuvants CpG-ODN on immune system of recombinant protein antigen Pfs25 by using this gel core liposomal system [49]. Liposomal formulations of several substances such as caryostatics, antibiotics, photosensitizers, enzymes, hormones, cytokines and nucleic acids (oligonucleotides for gene delivery) are currently among the promising results.

It is known that APC are a preferred alternative to muscle cells as targets for DNA vaccine uptake and expression. The administration of antigen-encoding plasmid DNA via liposomes could circumvent the need of muscle involvement and facilitate its uptake by APC, for instance those infiltrating the site of injection or in the lymphatics, at the same time protecting DNA from nuclease attack. The engineered liposomes offer effective delivery of their contents including DNA through non-invasive routes (oral and topical) thus eliminate disadvantages and phobia associated with needle injections. Transfection of APC with liposome-entrapped DNA could be promoted by the judicial choice of vesicle surface charge and lipid composition or by the co-entrapment of other adjuvants together with the plasmid DNA. The cationic lipids have been used to reduce the net negative charge on DNA plasmid-based gene expression systems in an attempt to reduce charge-charge repulsion at the surface of biological membranes. Moreover, such lipids form stable complex with DNA with high transfection efficiency. The pathway to transfection of cationic or pH-sensitive liposomes is thought to commence with endocytosis or membrane fusion. This is followed by destabilization of the endosomal membrane whereupon (either fusion of cationic liposome membrane with anionic endosomal membrane or destabilization of pH-sensitive vesicle membrane in low endosome pH environment) DNA is released into the cytosol (Figure 2).

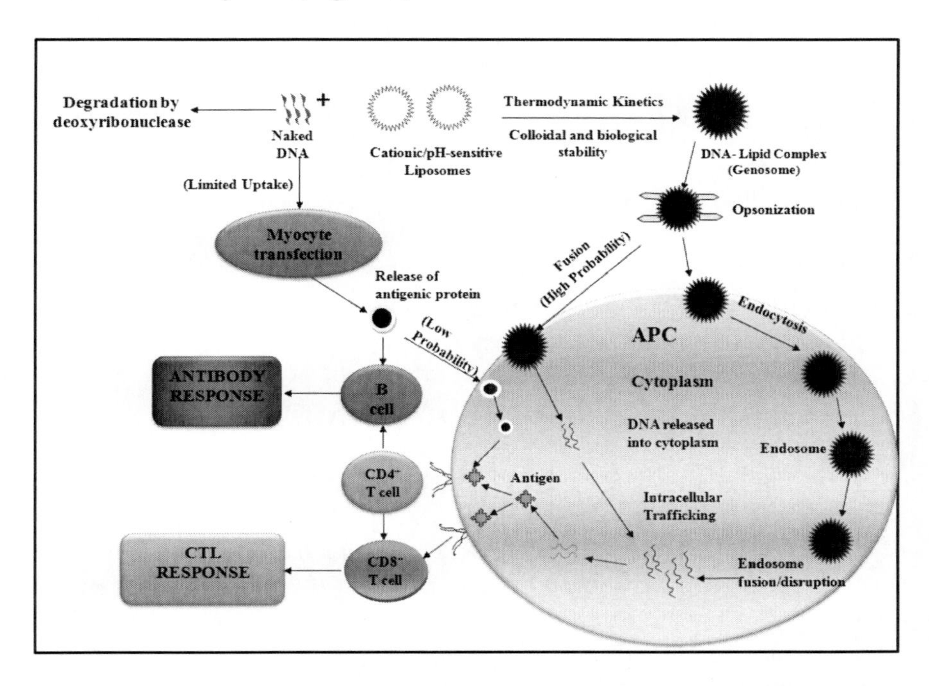

Figure 2. Schematic representation of proposed mechanism of DNA immunization via endocytic pathway. Naked DNA is taken up by a small number of myocytes after intramuscular injection, which are then transfected episomally. The produced antigen is released from the cells to interact with APC and thus induce immunity. In contrast, liposomal DNA interacts with APC directly and induces better immune response. It also protects DNA from degradation by deoxyribonuclease attack.

6. Topical Route: An Important Route for DNA Immunization

Although gene expression following direct injection of naked plasmid DNA into the skin has been illustrated, topical application of plasmid DNA represents an attractive and most innovative route of gene delivery. In an *in vivo* mouse model, the application of pEGFP-N1 DNA led to the generation of GFP-specific antibodies. The topical spray application of pEGFP-N1 liposomal DNA formulations is a suitable method for plasmid DNA delivery to the skin, yielding significant gene expression [50, 51]. Skin is an active immune surveillance site and shows both specific (immunity) and non-specific (inflammation) response for topical DNA vaccine [52]. Moreover, novel method (microporation) of topical immunization has revealed the high success rate with adeno-virus based vaccine [53]. The different parts of skin to be targeted, are follicular pathway, pilosebaceous pathway, normal pores present in the skin, lamellar lipid bodies and keratinocytes. Pilosebaceous unit is equipped with Langerhan's cells and Dendritic cells, which act as antigen presenting cells and present the processed antigen to migratory T cells.

7. Lipoplex (Liposome-DNA) Induced Toxicity

The intravenous injection of cationic lipid–DNA complexes is often accompanied by a dose-dependent toxicity. Piloerection and lethargy characters were observed in treated mice following the injections. The clinical analyses have shown a drop in the number of circulating lymphocytes (lymphopenia) and an increase in the serum levels of liver enzymes indicating liver damage [54] and Hepatic necrosis [55]. Usually these symptoms regressed back to normal within a few days after treatment, although several formulations were reported to be lethal above a certain dose at high lipid: DNA ratio [56]. The components of lipolexes had not displayed any toxicity even at much higher doses when administered alone, suggesting the damages relied on either the structure of the lipid–DNA complexes or lipoplex-associated features. The intravenous delivery induced toxicity by apoptosis of endothelial cells [56], and production of reactive oxygen intermediates [57] are glaring examples of lipolexes mediated lung toxicity. However, inspite of the toxicity associated with lipoplex-DNA, efficient delivery of plasmid DNA and subsequent GFP expression has been achieved using anionic lipoplexes [58].

Furthermore, TATp-liposomes and TATp liposome–DNA complexes were tested for comparative cytotoxicity assay performed with NIH-3T3 cells by using several different concentrations of DNA-free TATp-liposomes and Lipofectin. It is therefore inferred from the results obtained that at similar concentrations, low-cationic TATp liposomes with 10 mol % of DOTAP ((1, 2-Dioleoyl-3-Trimethyammonium-Propane) were nontoxic for the cells even after 24 h of incubation, whereas the same quantities of Lipofectin caused the death of 35–65% of cells in a concentration-dependent fashion [59]. The differences in transfection efficiency and toxicity are observed depending on the route of administration. The cellular and molecular mechanisms behind *in vivo* transfection should be elucidated to understand these differences. This knowledge will set the basis for further improvement to allow optimization of the formulations and of treatment regimens.

8. Liposome: A Versatile Drug Delivery Vehicle

The two major issues, pharmaco-immunotherapy, bio-distribution and targeting can be addressed by using liposomal formulation. An ideal liposomal formulation should be inert and stable to protect the delivered material from degradation and to extend its availability at the desired concentration. The following are among the important technological advantages of nanoparticles/liposomes as drug carriers: high stability (long shelf life); high carrier capacity (many drug/macro molecules can be incorporated in the particle matrix); feasibility of incorporation of both hydrophilic and hydrophobic substances; and feasibility of variable routes of administration, including oral administration and inhalation. These carriers can also be designed to enable controlled (sustained) drug release from the matrix (Liposome based marketed products, Table 1)

Table 1. Liposome based marketed products

Name	Trade name	Company	Indication
Liposomal amphotericin B	Abelcet	Enzon	Fungal infections
Liposomal amphotericin B	Ambisome	Gilead Sciences, Fujisawa Healthcare, Nexstar Pharmaceuticals	Fungal and protozoal infections
Liposomal cytarabine	Depocyt	Pacira (formerly Skye Pharma)	Malignant lymphomatous meningitis
Liposomal daunorubicin	DaunoXome	Gilead Sciences	HIV-related Kaposi's sarcoma
		Nexstar Pharmaceuticals	Kaposi's sarcoma
Liposomal doxorubicin	Myocet	Zeneus, Elan	Combination therapy with cyclophosphamide in metastatic breast cancer
	Myocet/Evacet	Drug Liposome	Metastatic breast cancer
Liposomal IRIV vaccine	Epaxal	Berna Biotech	Hepatitis A

Name	**Trade name**	**Company**	**Indication**
Liposomal IRIV vaccine	Inflexal V	Berna Biotech	Influenza
Liposomal morphine	DepoDur	SkyePharma, Endo	Postsurgical analgesia
Liposomal verteporfin	Visudyne	QLT, Novartis	Age-related macular degeneration, pathologic myopia, ocular histoplasmosis
Liposome-PEG doxorubicin	Doxil/Caelyx	Ortho Biotech, Schering-Plough,	HIV-related Kaposi's sarcoma, metastatic breast cancer, metastatic ovarian cancer
Liposome Doxorubicin	Doxil/Caelyx	Drug Sequus Pharmaceuticals	Kaposi's sarcoma
Liposome doxorubicin	Doxil	J&J ALZA	HIV-related Kaposi's sarcoma, metastatic breast cancer, metastatic ovarian cancer
Micellular estradiol	Estrasorb	Novavax	Menopausal therapy

9. Immunomodulation of Host Immunity by Clodronate-Loaded Liposome in Translational Biomedical Research

9.1. Liposomes Mediated Depletion of Macrophages (Suppression of Non-Adaptive Immune Responses) of Mice

Liposomes can be used as vehicles for intracellular delivery of drugs into phagocytic cells. Clodronate and propamidine, delivered into macrophages in this way, kills these cells as a result of intracellular accumulation and irreversible metabolic damage. The so-called liposome-mediated macrophage 'suicide' approach, which is based on this principle, is now frequently applied in studies aimed at unraveling macrophage function. The in vitro investigation of the mechanism of phagocytic cell death induced by liposome-encapsulated drugs was already performed in peritoneal macrophages [62]. We delivered liposomes encapsulated clodronate intracellularly to immunodeficient mice with an objective to achieving substantially high engraftment of human red blood cells to study P. falciparum [63-65]. All mice used were of the NOD/SCID background strain were immuno-compromised and capable of xeno-engraftment, but still retain some residual innate immune defenses. In addition, macrophages are thought to play a critical role in the early post-infection clearance of pathogen. Consequently, to aid in human cell engraftment and P. falciparum infection of human RBCs, mice underwent further immuno-modulation by treatment with intraperitoneal (IP) injected clodronate-loaded liposomes. Clodronate-loaded liposomes are lipid vesicles that contain clodronate (i.e., dichloromethylenediphosphonate), a nontoxic bisphosphonate that was developed for human clinical applications. As macrophages ingest and digest the liposome, the clodronate is released within the macrophage, accumulates within the macrophage, and triggers apoptosis (i.e., programmed cell death) reducing the number of macrophages (Table 2: Immunomodulatory reagents/chemicals to further reduce the residual immune responses).

Table 2. Various immune suppressants to control innate immunity

Experiments Performed Using I.P. Protocol With Various Immunomodulatory Reagent					
Protocol tested	**Dose**	**Nb of mouse**	**% of sucrose(more than 2 days**	**Paracitemia length average (days)**	**Best parasitemia (days)**
DSMO	5 %	18	88.8	7.18	12
TGFβ	100 ng/day	17	23.5	7.25	8
	100 μg/day	3	66.6	10	13
Splenctomy		5	60	7	10
Cyclophopshamide	75 mg/Kg	7	100	7.6	9
	50 mg/Kg	12	41.6	6.8	9
Coinfection *P.Chabaudi* P.Falciparum		7	71.42	11	24
Coinfection *P.Yoellii P.Falciparum*		52	90.24	11.09	34
NAC	100 mg/Kg	25	56	11.07	19
Vitamin E	200 mg/kg	13	77	8.25	34
Trolox	4 mg/Kg	5	60	3.85	6
Anti-NK(TMBβ-1)	1 mg	15	53.3	4.12	8
Futhan	200 μg/day	4	50	2.75	4
Bleeding		20	35	7.42	14
P.Falciparum with various amount	0.3	2	100	2	2
	1%	2	100	4	4
	5%	2	100	5.5	6
	7%	2	100	4	4
	10%	2	100	5.5	6
pABA	400 mg/Kg	4	100	4.5	5
Folinic acid	mg/Kg	4	100	4.5	5

Coinfection *P. Choaudi* and *P. Yoellii*, NAC and Vitamin E seem to have beneficial effect in *P. Falciparum* survival; however, results are very heterogenous from one mouse to other and from one experiment to other.

9.2. Optimization of Humanized Mice: Clodronate-Liposome Further Reduces Non-Adaptive Immunity of Immuno-deficient Mice

The present results suggest that macrophage depletion (control of residual non-adaptive immune responses) by clodronate-loaded liposomes is an inevitable requirement to achieving humanized mouse model (Pf-NSG-IV) to study asexual blood stage infection of P. falciparum (Figure 3 and Figure 4). The liposome- mediated macrophage 'suicide' approach, based on depletion of macrophages by liposome mediated intraphagocytic delivery and accumulation of drugs is now commonly applied in studies focusing on the elucidation of macrophage function [62]

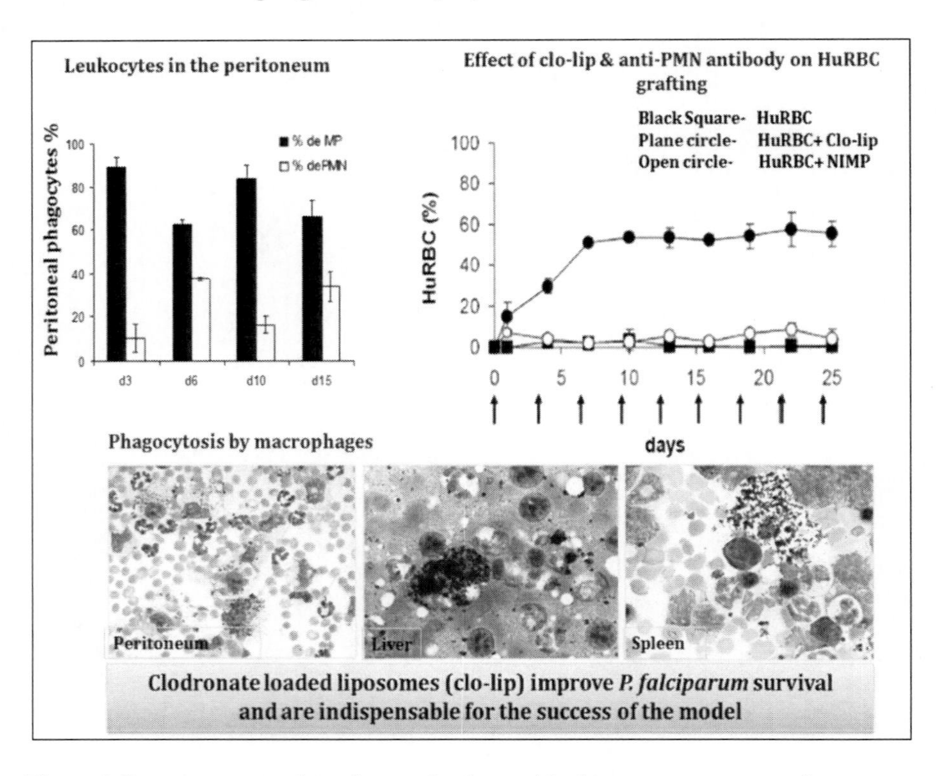

Figure 3. Immunosuppression of non-adaptive residual immune responses of immunodeficient mice by the sustained delivery of Clodronate via liposomes.

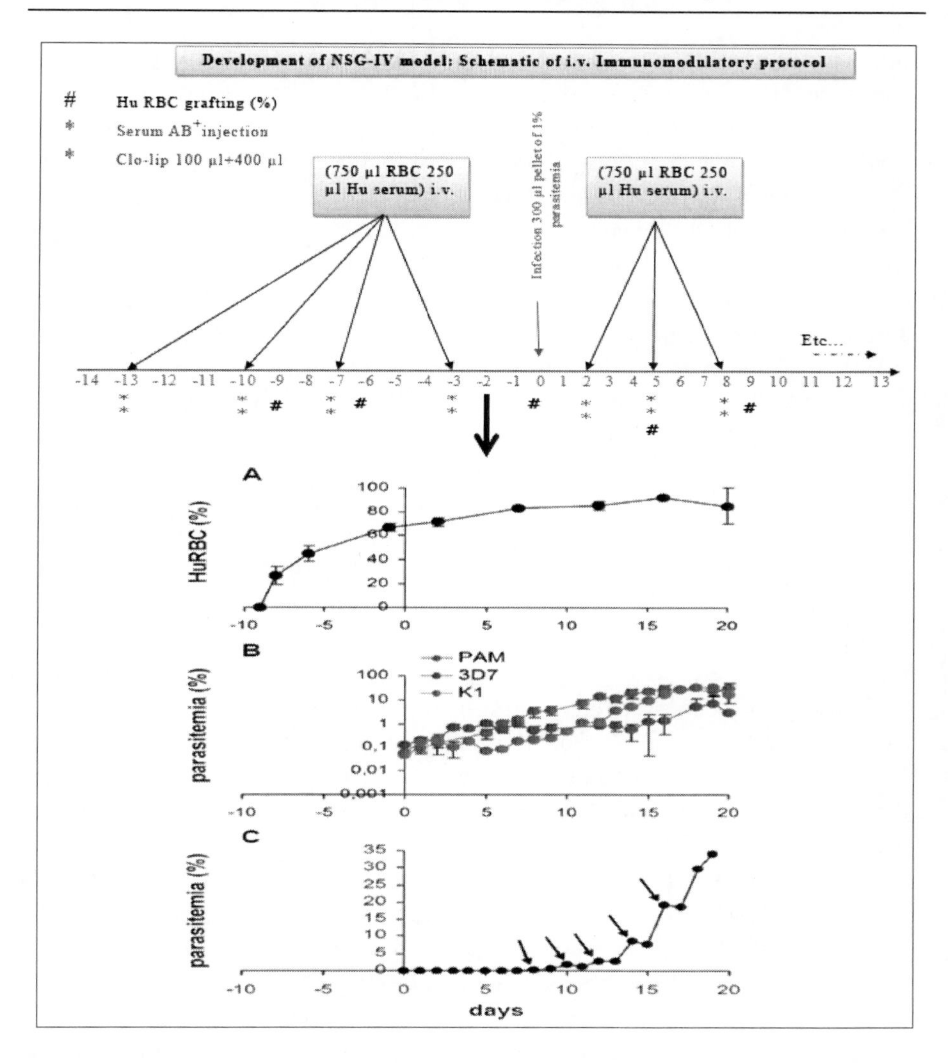

Figure 4. Schematic for the development of optimized Pf-NSG-IV mice.

10. Expert Commentary and Future Perspectives

The role of novel carrier(s) in targeted and controlled delivery of antigen, proteins and plasmid DNA needs more attention to explore the possibility of effective vaccine against malaria. The stage and species-specific insufficient immunity developed by the attenuated sporozoite, synthetic and recombinant immunogenic peptide has hampered the attempts to develop vaccine. Also, existence of potent and biocompatible adjuvant is in question due to scarce availability of efficient adjuvant formulation. Currently most of the work carried out in the direction of proposed research is based upon single unit DNA vaccination. The developed multistage vaccine, NYVAC-Pf7 is a single genome containing genes encoding seven *Plasmodium falciparum* antigens (two are derived from the sporozoite stage of parasite life cycle (CSP and sporozoite surface protein 2 (PfSSP2)), one from the liver stage (liver stage antigen 1 (LSA1)), three from the blood stage (merozoite surface protein 1 (MSP1), serine repeat antigen (SERA), and AMA-1), and one from the sexual stage (25-kDa sexual- stage antigen (Pfs25)). The intent was to express multiple antigens from *P. falciparum* to induce immunity in recipient, but only four genes encoding the concern antigen could express.

The administration of antigen-encoding plasmid DNA via engineered liposomes (ligand anchoring of liposomes to targeting dendritic cells) could circumvent the need of muscle involvement and facilitate its uptake by APC. This offers the effective delivery of their contents including DNA through non-invasive routes (oral and topical) thus eliminate the disadvantages and phobia associated with needle injections. There are many alternative approaches to the oral delivery (non-invasive route), and our laboratory has explored various versions of delivery systems for the mucosal immunization. Moreover, the work done on malaria vaccine development so far has provided the promising results with the topical route. There are various approaches to the delivery of the vaccine such as liposome, virosome, microparticle and niosomes. The versatility and delivery potential of engineered liposome (pH sensitive liposome) has been revealed and its role in intracellular cytosolic delivery of PfMSP-1_{19} has been advocated. The enhanced immunogenicity of a soluble malaria antigen has also been reported [47], and further study might open new vistas to developing blood stage malaria vaccine. We have compared various formulations of MSP-1 construct of DNA vaccine with and without liposome and achieved promising and significant results that attest the potential of this novel carrier [unpublished data]. The potential approach to the cytosolic delivery of vaccine is the encapsulation/entrapment of antigen/DNA into the lipid-based formulation of pH sensitive liposome. Lipid based delivery systems can be manipulated to enhance the efficacy of topically administered vaccine in number of ways: they can protect antigen or DNA from degradation, concentrate them in one area of tissue for better presentation, targeted delivery as their surface can be coated (either by O-palmitoylmannan or cholesterol mannan for mannosylation or CD11c ligand specific for DCs) by the ligands specific for the dendritic cell receptors.

Immunization always does not stimulate immunity because of the insufficient elicitation of immune responses. Such limitations have spurred the development of new adjuvant and antigen delivery systems. Adjuvant plays an important role in enhancing the efficacy of vaccines. Recombinant proteins or synthetic peptides are safer than crude inactivated microorganisms, but less immunogenic. This limitation may be overcome by using specific adjuvant. The adjuvant selection depends on the several criteria such as the target species antigens, type of desired immune response, route of administration or duration of immunity. So far biodegradable polymers, particularly PLGA, have been used considerably because of their well-known degradation properties; however, this area requires an additional effort for analytical characterization of protein/DNA encapsulated or adsorbed microparticles. In addition, advanced methods for protein characterization is in demand to approach problem of protein stabilization in polymer based delivery systems. A significant progress has been made recently with biodegradable polymers, mainly PLGA and various approaches are being considered for the effective stabilization of proteins in microparticles during preparation process. In conclusion, an efficient delivery vehicle combined with an effective adjuvant administered through an optimal route of immunization, will ultimately allow for the development of a successful needle free (topical) vaccine in humans. Various versions of engineered liposomes have been employed and substantial results have been attained in vaccine development research. In addition liposome loaded with clodronate drug have shown sizeable success in suppressing non-adaptive immune responses that helped developing a humanized mice to study immunology and pathophysiology of most deadliest human parasite, P. falciparum.

FINANCIAL AND COMPETING INTEREST DISCLOSURE

The research work was supported by various grants from Department of Biotechnology, Council of Scientific and Industrial Research (CSIR) and University Grant Commission, New Delhi, India. *In vivo* animal work was funded by Institute Pasteur, Paris, France. The authors have no other relevant affiliations or financial involvement with any organization or entity with a financial interest in or financial conflict with the subject matter or material discussed in the manuscript apart from those disclosed. No writing assistance was utilized in the production of this manuscript.

REFERENCES

[1] WHO, World Malaria Report 2010. www.who.int/malaria/world_malaria_report_2010/en/index.html (2010).

[2] B. Greenwood, Malaria vaccines. Evaluation and implementation, *Acta. Trop.* 95 (2005) 298–304.

[3] N.J. White, Drug resistance in malaria, *British Medical Bulletin* 54 (1998) 703-715.

[4] C.F. Curtis, Should the use of DDT be revived for malaria vector control? *Biomedica.* 22 (2002) 455-461.

[5] E. Malkin, F. Dubovsky, M. Moree, Progress towards the development of malaria vaccines, *Trends Parasitol.* 22 (2006) 292–295.

[6] R.S. Nussenbzweig, J. Vanderberg, H. Most, C. Orton, Protective immunity produced by the injection of X-irradiated sporozoite of *Plasmodium berghei, Nature* 216(1967) 160- 162.

[7] D.F. Clyde, V.C. McCarthy, R.M. Miller, R.B. Hornick, Specificity of protection of man immunized against sporozoite induced *falciparum* malaria, *Am. J. Med. Sci.* 266 (1973a)398- 403.

[8] D.F. Clyde, V.C. McCarthy, R.M. Miller, J.P. Vanderberg, Specificity of protection of man immunized against sporozoite induced *falciparum* malaria, *Am. J. Med. Sci.* 266(1973b) 169-177.

[9] D.F. Clyde, V.C. McCarthy, R.M. Miller, W.E. Woodward, Immunization of man against *falciparum* and *vivax* malaria by use of attenuated sporozoites, *Am. Trop. Med. Hyg.* 24 (1975) 397- 401.

[10] R.W. Gwadz, A.H. Cochrane, V. Nussenbzweig, R.S. Nussenbzweig, Preliminary studies on vaccination of rhesus monkeys with irradiated sporozoites of *Plasmodium knowleski* and characterization of surface antigens of these parasites, *Bull. World. Health Organ.* 57 (1979) 165-173.

[11] Malcolm J. Gardner, Neil Hall, Eula Fung, Owen White, Matthew Berriman and Bart Barrell. Genome sequence of the human malaria parasite *Plasmodium falciparum. Nature* 419, 498-511 (2002)

[12] D.L. Doolan, S.L. Hoffman, DNA based vaccines against malaria: status and promise of the multistage malaria DNA Vaccine Operation, *Int. J. Parasitol.* 31(2006) 753-762.

[13] W.E. Collins, J.W. Barnwell, Plasmodium knowlesi: finally being recognized, *The Journal of infectious diseases* 199(2009) 1107-1108.
[14] J. Cox-Singh, T.M. Davis, K.S. Lee, S.S. Shamsul, A. Matusop, S. Ratnam, H.A. Rahman, D.J. Conway, B. Singh, Plasmodium knowlesi malaria in human is widely distributed and potentially life threatening, *Clin. Infect. Dis.* 46(2008) 165-171.
[15] B. Singh, L. Kim Sung, A. Matusop, A. Radhakrishnan, S.S. Shamsul, J. Cox-Singh, A. Thomas, D.J. Conway, A large focus of naturally acquired Plasmodium knowlesi infections in human beings, *Lancet* 363(2004) 1017-1024.
[16] N.J. White, Plasmodium knowlesi: the fifth human malaria parasite. *Clin. Infect. Dis*. 46(2008a)172-173.
[17] F. Dubovsky, N.R. Rabinovich, Malaria vaccines. In: Plotkin SA, Orenstein WA, editors. *Vaccines*. 4th ed. Philadelphia: Saunders, 2004, 1283-1289.
[18] M.P. Girard, Z.H. Reed, M. Friede, M.P. Kieny, A review of human vaccine research and development: Malaria, *Vaccine* 25 (2007) 1567-1580.
[19] M.A. Herrera, S. Herrera, *Plasmodium vivax* malaria vaccine development, Mol. Immunol. 38 (2001) 443-455.
[20] I.E. McGregor, The passive transfer of human malarial immunity, *Am. J. Trop. Med. Hyg*. 13(1964) 237–239.
[21] D.F. Clyde, V.C. McCarthy, M.R. Miller, W.F. Woodward, Immunization of man against *falciparum* and *vivax*malaria by use of attenuated sporozoites, *Am. J. Trop. Med. Hyg.* 24(1975) 397–401.
[22] K.H. Rieckmann, R.L. Beaudoin, J.S. Cassells, K.W. Sell, Use of attenuated sporozoites in the immunization of human volunteers against *falciparum* malaria. *Bull. World Health Organ.* 57 (1979) 261–265.
[23] G.A. González, Y.N. Molano, E.M. Esteban, D. Rodríguez, J.R. Rodríguez, P. Palese, A. García-Sastre, R.S. Nussenzweig. Induction of protective immunity against malaria by priming-boosting immunization with recombinant cold-adapted influenza and modified vaccinia Ankara viruses expressing a CD8+-T-cell epitope derived from the circumsporozoite protein of Plasmodium yoelii, *J. Virol.* 77 (2003) 11859-66.
[24] M. Tsuji, C.C. Bergmann, Y. Takita-Sonoda, K. Murata, E.G. Rodrigues, R.S. Nussenzweig, F. Zavala, Recombinant Sindbis viruses expressing a cytotoxic T-lymphocyte epitope of a malaria parasite or of

influenza virus elicit protection against the corresponding pathogen in mice, *J.Virol.* 72 (1998) 6907-10.

[25] S.E. Parker, D. Monteith, H. Horton, R. Hof, P. Hernandez, A. Vilalta, Safety of a GM-CSF adjuvant-plasmid DNA malaria vaccine, *GeneTher.* 8 (2001)1011–1023.

[26] R. Wang, D.L. Doolan, T.P. Le, R.C. Hedstrom, K.M. Coonan, Y. Charoenvit, Induction of antigen-specific cytotoxic T lymphocytes in humans by a malaria DNA vaccine, *Science* 282 (1998) 476–480.

[27] R. Wang, J. Epstein, F.M. Baraceros, E.J. Gorak, Y. Charoenvit, D.J. Carucci, Induction of CD4 (+) T cell-dependent CD8 (+) type 1 responses in humans by a malaria DNA vaccine, *Proc. Natl. Acad. Sci. U.S.A.* 98 (2001) 10817–10822.

[28] A.C. Moore, A.V. Hill, Progress in DNA-based heterologous prime-boost immunization strategies for malaria, *Immunol. Rev.* 199 (2004)126–143.

[29] J.D. Kurtis, M.R. Hollingdale, A.J. Luty, D.E. Lanar, U. Krzych, P.E. Duffy, Pre-erythrocytic immunity to *Plasmodium falciparum*: the case for an LSA-1 vaccine, *Trends Parasitol.*17(2001) 219–223.

[30] P. Daubersies, A.W. Thomas, P. Millet, K. Brahimi, J.A. Langermans, B. Ollomo, L. BenMohamed, B. Slierendregt, W. Eling, A. Van Belkum, G. Dubreuil, J.F. Meis, C. Guérin-Marchand, S. Cayphas, J. Cohen, H. Gras-Masse, P. Druilhe, Protection against *Plasmodium falciparum* malaria in chimpanzees by immunization with the conserved pre-erythrocytic liver-stage antigen 3, *Nat. Med.*6(2000)1258–1263.

[31] D.A. Barnes, W. Wollish, R.G. Nelson, J.H. Leech, C. Petersen, *Plasmodium falciparum*: D260, an intra-erythrocytic parasite protein, is a member of the glutamic acid dipeptide-repeat family of proteins, *Exp.Parasitol.*81 (1995)79–89.

[32] A.F. Egan, J. Morris, G. Barnish, Clinical immunity to *Plasmodium falciparum* malaria is associated with serum antibodies to the 19-kDa C-terminal fragment of the merozoite surface antigen, PfMSP-1, *J. Infect. Dis.*173 (1996)765–769.

[33] A.F. Egan, P. Burghaus, P. Druilhe, A.A. Holder, E.M. Riley, Human antibodies to the 19 kDaC-terminal fragment of *Plasmodium falciparum* merozoite surface protein 1 inhibit parasite growth *in vitro*, *Parasite Immunol.*21(1999) 133–139.

[34] R.A. O'Donnell, T.F. de Koning-Ward, R.A. Burt, Antibodies against merozoite surface protein (msp)-1(19) are a major component of the

invasion-inhibitory response in individuals immune to malaria, *J. Exp. Med.*193(2001)1403–1412.
[35] A.A. Holder, J.A. Guevara Patino, C. Uthaipibull, Merozoite surface protein 1, immune evasion, and vaccines against asexual blood stage malaria, *Parasitologia* 41(1999)409–414.
[36] D.C. Kaslow, Transmission-Blocking Vaccine. In: Hoffman, S.L (Ed.), Malaria Vaccine Development: A Multi-Immune Response Approach. *American Society for Microbiology*, Washington, DC, 1996, pp. 181–227.
[37] R. Carter, K.N. Mendis, L.H. Miller, L. Molineaux, A. Saul, Malaria transmission-blocking vaccines—how can their development be supported? *Nat. Med.* 6 (2000) 241–244.
[38] H. Hisaeda, A.W. Stowers, T. Tsuboi, W.E. Collins, J.S. Sattabongkot, N. Suwanabun, Antibodies to malaria vaccine candidates Pvs25 and Pvs28 completely block the ability of *Plasmodium vivax*to infect mosquitoes, *Infect. Immun.* 68 (2000) 6618–6623.
[39] P.J. Bustamante, D.C. Woodruff, J. Oh, D.B. Keister, O. Muratova, K.C. Williamson, Differential ability of specific regions of *Plasmodium falciparum* sexual-stage antigen, Pfs230, to induce malaria transmission-blocking immunity, *Parasite Immunol.* 22 (2000)373–380.
[40] D.G. Becker, V. Moulin, B. Pajak, C. Bruck, M. Francotte, C. Thiriart, J. Urbain, M. Moser, The adjuvant monophosphoryl lipid A increases the function of antigen-presenting cells, *Int.Immunol.* 12 (2000) 807-815.
[41] J. Aucouturier, L. Dupuis, V.Ganne, Adjuvant designed for veterinary and human vaccines, *Vaccine* 19(2001) 2666-2672.
[42] Lindahl T, Joseph A. G and Edelman, GM. Deoxyribonucleaseiv: a new exonuclease from mammalian tissues. *PNAS* (1968) 597-603
[43] A.D. Bangham, M.M. Standish, N. Miller Cation permeability of phospholipid model membranes: effect of narcotics, *Nature* 208, 1295-1297 (1965).
[44] A.G. Allison, G. Gregoriadis, Liposomes as immunological adjuvants, *Nature* 252(1974) 252.
[45] I. Rosenkrands, M.E. Agger, W.A. Olsen, S.K. Korsholm, S.C. Andersen, T.K. Jensen, P. Andersen, Cationic Liposomes Containing Mycobacterial Lipids: a New Powerful Th1 Adjuvant System, *Infect. Immun.* 73(2005)5817–5826.
[46] M. Owais, C.M. Gupta, Liposome-mediated cytosolic delivery of macromolecules and its possible use in vaccine development, Eur. *J. Biochem.* 267(2000) 3946-3956.

[47] S.P. Vyas, R.S. Jadon, A.K. Goyal, N. Mishra, P.N. Gupta, K. Khatri, R. Tyagi, pH sensitive liposomes enhances immunogenicity of 19 kDa carboxyl-terminal fragment of *Plasmodium falciparum, Int. J. Pharm. Sci. Nanotech.* 1 (2007) 78-86.

[48] S. Tiwari, A.K. Goyal, K. Khatri, P.N. Gupta, N. Mishra, S.P. Vyas, Gel core liposomes: an advanced carrier for improved vaccine delivery. *J. Microencapsulation* 26 (2009) 75-82.

[49] S. Tiwari, A.K. Goyal, N. Mishra, K.Khatri, B.Vaidya, A. Mehta, Y. Wu, S.P. Vyas, Development and characterization of novel carrier gel core liposomes based transmission blocking malaria vaccine. *J. Cont. Release* 140 (2009) 157-165.

[50] N. Meykadeh, A. Mirmohammadsadegh, Z. Wang, E.B. Schakarjan, U.R. Hengge, Topical application of plasmid DNA to mouse and human skin, *J. Mol. Med.* 83(2005) 897-903.

[51] M.J. Choi, H.I. Maibach, Topical vaccination of DNA antigens: Topical Delivery of DNA antigens, *Skin Pharmacol Appl. Skin Physiol.* 16 (2003) 271-282.

[52] R.P. Singh, P. Singh, V. Mishra, D. Prabakaran, S.P. Vyas, Vesicular systems for non-invasive topical immunization: rationale and prospects, *Indian J. Pharmacol.* 34 (2002) 301-310.

[53] J. Bramson, K. Dayball, C. Evelegh, Y.H. Wan, D. Page, A. Smith, Enabling topical immunization via microporation: a novel method for pain free and needle free delivery of adenovirus-based vaccines, *Gene Ther.* 10 (2003) 251–260.

[54] J.D. Toussignant, A.L. Gates, L.A. Ingram, C.L. Johnson, J.B. Nietupski, S.H. Chen, S.J. Eastman, R.K. Scheule, Comprehensive analysis of the acute toxicities induced by systemic administration of cationic lipid:plasmid DNA complexes in mice, *Hum. Gene Ther.*11(2000) 2493–2513.

[55] Y.K. Song, F. Liu, S. Chu, D. Liu, Characterization of cationic liposome-mediated gene transfer *in vivo* by intravenous administration, *Hum. Gene Ther.*8 (1997)1585–1594.

[56] S. Li, P.S. Wu, M. Whitmore, E.J. Loeffert, L. Wang, S.C. Watkins, B.R. Pitt, L. Huang, Effect of immune response on gene transfer to the lung via systemic administration of cationic lipid vectors, *Am. J. Physiol.* 276 (1999) L796–L804.

[57] S. Dokka, D. Toledo, X. Shi, V. Castranova, Y. Rojanasakul, Oxygen radical-mediated pulmonary toxicity induced by some cationic liposomes, *Pharm. Res.*17 (2000) 521–525.

[58] Patil SD, Rhodes DG and Burgess DJ. Anionic Liposomal Delivery System for DNA Transfection. *The AAPS Journal* 6 (2004) 1-10.

[59] V.P. Torchilin, T.S. Levchenko, R. Rammohan, N. Volodina, B.P. Sternberg, G.M.G. D'Souza, Cell transfection in vitro and in vivo with non-toxic TAT peptide-liposome–DNA complexes, *Proc. Natl. Acad. Sci. U.S.A.* 100 (2003) 1972-1977.

[60] D. Felnerova, J.F. Viret, R. Glück, C. Moser, Liposomes and virosomes as delivery systems for antigens, nucleic acids and drugs, *Curr. Opin. Biotechnol.* 15 (2004) 518-29.

[61] L. Zhang, F.X. Gu, J.M. Chan, A.Z. Wang, R.S. Langer, O.C. Farokhzad, Nanoparticles in Medicine: *Therapeutic Applications and Developments,Clin. Pharmacol. Ther.* 83 (2008) 761-9.

[62] van Rooijen, N, Sanders A, van den Berg TK. Apoptosis of macrophages induced by liposome-mediated intracellular delivery of clodronate and propamidine. *Journal of Immunological Methods* 193 (1996) 93-99

[63] Arnold L, Tyagi RK, Mejia P, Van Rooijen N, Pérignon JL, Druilhe P. Analysis of innate defences against Plasmodium falciparum in immunodeficient mice. *Malar J.* 2010 Jul 9; 9:197.

[64] Arnold L, Tyagi RK, Meija P, Swetman C, Gleeson J, Pérignon JL, Druilhe P. Further improvements of the P. falciparum humanized mouse model. *PLoS One.* 2011 Mar 31; 6(3): e18045.

[65] Tyagi RK, Garg NK, Sahu T. Vaccination Strategies against Malaria: novel carrier(s) more than a tour de force. *J Control Release.* 2012 Aug 20;162 (1):242-54.

In: Advances in Liposomes Research
Editor: Lauren Finney
ISBN: 978-1-63117-074-4

Chapter 2

LIPOSOMAL DELIVERY OF ANTIMICROBIAL AGENTS IN ADVANCES IN LIPOSOME RESEARCH

Claire Martin[1,2*], Wan Li Low[3], Abhishek Gupta[1], Mohd Cairul Iqbal Mohd Amin[4], Iza Radecka[2,3], Prem Raj[1], Stephen Britland[1,2] and Ken Kenward[1]

[1]Department of Pharmacy
[2]Research Institute in Healthcare Science
[3]Department of Biology, Chemistry and Forensic Science,
Faculty of Science and Engineering, University of Wolverhampton,
Wulfruna Street, Wolverhampton, UK
[4]Faculty of Pharmacy, Universiti Kebangsaan Malaysia,
Jalan Raja Muda Abd Aziz, Kuala Lumpur, Malaysia

ABSTRACT

Chronic and slow/non-healing wounds require extensive management to reduce the repair and recovery time. Wound dressings and devices are often designed to suit varying wound characteristics and strategically manage the complexity of different wound types. The main challenges in managing the chronic wound environment include:

---

* Author for correspondence: Tel.: +44 (0) 1902 322 149; Email: Claire.martin2@wlv.ac.uk.

- delivery of sufficient antimicrobial agent to maintain bioavailability at biocidal concentrations
- control of the quantity of wound exudate whilst promoting/maintaining the availability of pro-healing factors
- reduction of the risk of uneven antimicrobial deposition, lowering the risk of localized toxicity
- improvement in the ease of antimicrobial and wound dressing application
- reduction of the frequency of dressing changes thus minimising patient discomfort and avoid risk opportunity for further infection

Topical administration of agents can require penetration through dead matter, purulent exudates and scar tissue as well as the dermis, which serves as the first line of defence. The dermal barrier has low permeability to large hydrophilic entities but will selectively allow permeation of small lipophilic molecules. Whilst essential for maintenance of host homeostasis, this limited permeability dramatically restricts delivery of many antimicrobial agents both to the wound surface as well as into the various layers of the dermis. These issues can be reduced with the aid of controlled release drug delivery systems such as liposomes, which can improve targeting, efficacy and the biopharmaceutical properties of the antimicrobial agent. Liposomes are biocompatible, biodegradable, lipid bilayer vesicles with a large aqueous inner-core for encapsulation and delivery of active agents. Encapsulation of antimicrobial agents in liposomes provides protection from enzymatic and immunological inactivation. Additionally, the liposome's capacity to bind water may aid moisture retention, which promotes an environment that is highly conducive to tissue repair. The capacity to transport both hydrophilic and hydrophobic materials, has allowed a wide range of pharmaceutical formulations to be incorporated into liposome vesicles. In terms of encapsulation, agents with varying lipophilicities can be sequestered within the phospholipid bilayer (hydrophobic), entrapped in the inner core (hydrophilic), as well as in the inner and outer bilayer interface (hydrophilic) of the liposome. This ability of liposomes to encapsulate antimicrobial agents with a broad range of physicochemical properties makes them valuable in wound management applications. This chapter will examine the diverse antimicrobial payloads, including antibiotics, antifungals, natural products and essential oils, which are amenable to liposome delivery and show enhanced therapeutic outcomes. The advantages of liposome encapsulated antimicrobials are their potential to achieve effective drug delivery whilst reducing problems related to targeting, biodistribution and bioavailability of microbiocidal agents.

INTRODUCTION: WOUNDS AND WOUND HEALING

Wound healing is a complex cascading event involving cellular, enzymatic and biochemical pathways, spanning from the time the skin is damaged until the wound is completely healed [Fonder et al., 2008; Ovington, 2007]. Maintenance of healthy wound site homeostasis is thus important to maximize wound healing capacity, especially in immunocompromised patients or those with underlying chronic health conditions. The events in wound healing have been divided into four main stages, namely exudative, resorptive, proliferative and regenerative phase [Stojadinovic et al., 2008; Wild et al., 2010; Gurtner et al., 2008; Shaw and Martin, 2009] as detailed in Figure 1. In the exudative phase, haemostasis and clot formation occurs. The ruptured cells and vessels at wound edges release stress signals including damage-associated molecular pattern molecules (DAMPS). These stress signals initiate vasoconstriction, trigger platelets to release inflammatory response mediators and activate the clotting cascade. The clot formed (fibrin matrix) provides support for infiltrating inflammatory cells and triggers the release of inflammatory mediators. During the resorptive phase, inflammatory responses, redness, swelling, heat, pain and loss of function occur in the resorptive phase. In contrast to the exudative phase, vasodilation facilitates the leakage of neutrophils and macrophages into the wound site. These cells aid in the removal of bacterial cells and damaged extracellular matrix molecules (*via* phagocytosis and generation of reactive oxygen species) to facilitate the migration of tissue repair molecules.

In the proliferative phase, angiogenesis occurs to provide oxygen and nutrients to the growing tissues. Wound closure is initiated by wound contraction and migration of epithelial cells from the wound edge. Progressive wound closure is accompanied by the formation of provisional matrix (type III collagen), granulation tissues (randomly deposited collagen, capillaries and fibroblasts), as well as the proliferation of keratinocytes and endothelial cells. In the final stage of wound healing, re-epithelialisation occurs to ensure full closure of the wound and a scar is formed. In this regenerative phase, functional networks of blood vessels are refined whilst neutrophils and macrophages clear from the site. Tissue remodelling takes place to arrange the newly synthesized type I collagens to replace the provisional matrix (type III collagen) to increase tensile strength of the new structure.

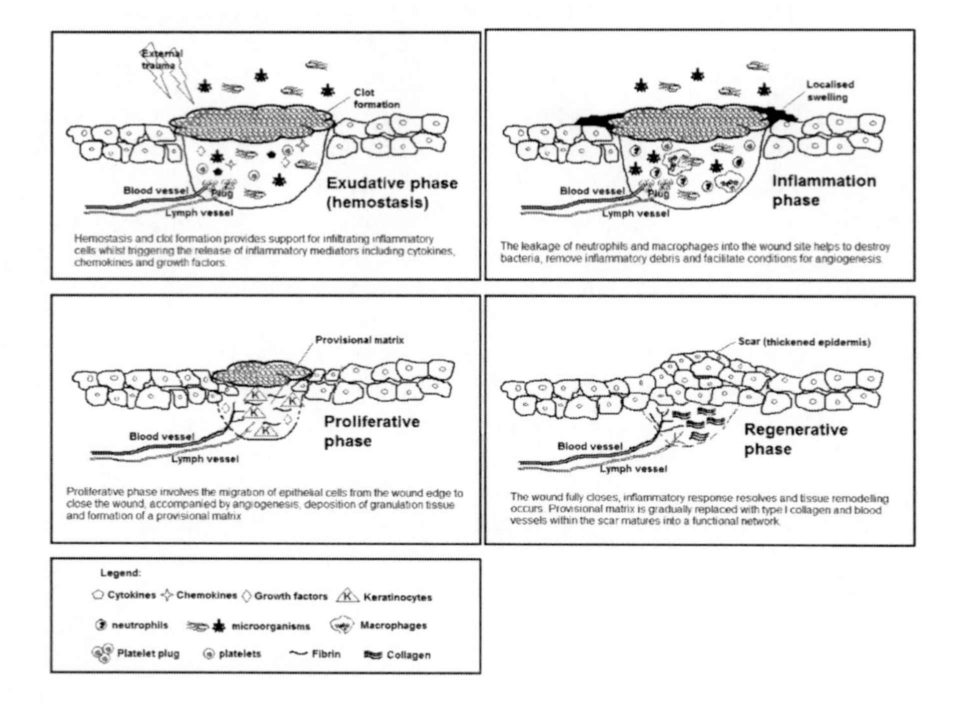

Figure 1. The four stages of wound healing: Exudative, inflammatory, proliferative and regenerative.

Generally, wound healing follows this sequence but, being non-linear, the stages may move forwards and backwards, based on intrinsic and extrinsic factors as well as the severity of the wound [Wild et al., 2010]. The rate of wound healing differs between individuals and is influenced by factors such as type and depth of wound, age, nutrition, immune status, underlying health conditions as well as local microbial burden.

Microbial infection in particular retards wound healing by increasing the bio-burden at wound sites, thus stalling the normal process at the inflammatory phase. It is common for chronic wounds to become contaminated and colonized by microorganisms. Such colonization by microorganisms, especially common skin commensals such as *Staphylococcus epidermidis* and *Corynebacterium* species, does not usually impair wound healing, provided the population remains below the critical threshold of approximately 10^5 cells per gram of wound tissue [Stojadinovic et al., 2008]. Their presence and production of proteolytic enzymes may help to stimulate the activity of neutrophils, thereby encouraging an inflammatory response which may facilitate wound healing [Schultz et al., 2003]. Cutaneous wounds offer a favourable (moist, warm, nutritious) environment to support bacterial growth and proliferation, which may lead to an imbalance of the commensal microflora resulting in heavy colonization and infection [Gallant-Behm et al., 2005; Bowler et al., 2001]. When acute wounds become infected and reach critical colonization by pathogenic microorganisms, the stimulated pro-inflammatory environment (due to microbial production of toxins, proteases or pro-inflammatory molecules), will stop the process of wound healing and the site develops into a chronic wound [Gallant-Behm et al., 2005; Stojadinovic et al., 2008]. Critical colonization is defined as a condition in which bacterial infection exceeds the ability of the host's immune system to eliminate further proliferation and colonization [Stojadinovic et al., 2008].

With certain types of wounds, e.g., burns, the leading causes of death are septic shock and organ dysfunction [Church et al., 2006]. Systemic infections are the most common complication and generally result from wounds colonised by invasive species from the skin, e.g., *Staphylococcus aureus*, or the gastrointestinal tract, *Pseudomonas aeruginosa* and *Candida albicans*. Another complication is the development of pneumonia, which can result from thermal injury, aspiration, atelectasis (collapsed) and hypostatic (fluid build-up) pulmonary affects. In addition, patients who require intubation also display a high incidence of ventilator-associated pneumonia (VAP) and those with bacteraemia, which can lead to secondary seeding of infection in the lungs disseminated by circulating microorganisms. Other sources of systemic infection include:

- urinary tract which can be associated with urogenital catheterisation
- intravenous and intra-arterial lines (both central and peripheral)
- suppurating thrombophlebitis (positive diagnosis of bacteraemia concurrent with venous thrombosis and inflammation)
- myonecrosis (deep tissue injury and infection)
- pyomyositis (skeletal muscle infection and the development of pus-filled abscesses) [Church et al., 2006]

This review therefore covers not only liposomal formulations used in the treatment of topical wounds, but also common systemic infections in distal organs, such as the lungs, which may occur secondary to the original site of infection.

LIPOSOMES

Liposomes were first described in the 1960s, but it was the 1970s before their potential for drug delivery was recognised. Their main advantage is improving the efficacy and therapeutic index of active drugs whilst reducing localized toxicity [Lian and Ho, 2001]. Development of liposomes for topical delivery investigated targeting, retention and stability of the active agent, as well as penetration and compartmentalization into different layers of the skin [De Leeuw et al., 2009; Gregoriadis, 1995; Mura et al., 2009].

Topical administration of agents requires penetration through the skin, which serves as the first line of defence. Under normal conditions, the uppermost layer of the skin, the stratum corneum which consists of keratinocytes in a lipid-rich matrix , serves as a barrier with low permeability [Karande and Mitragotri, 2009; Mura et al., 2009]. This barrier also functions as a regulator for the movement of water into and out of the body, and selectively allows permeation of small lipophilic molecules with molecular weight less than 500 Da [Bos and Meinardi, 2000; Karande and Mitragotri, 2009]. Liposomes with an average diameter of 0.05-5.0 μm are therefore a suitable system for transdermal or topical drug delivery [De Leeuw et al., 2009; Pavelic et al., 2005].

The complex mixture of phagocytes, inflammatory mediators, hydrolytic enzymes, reactive oxygen species and bacteria in a wound will affect the activity of antimicrobial agents. Encapsulation of antimicrobial agents in liposomes provides protection from enzymatic and immunological inactivation [Drulis-Kawa and Dorotkiewicz-Jach, 2010]. Additionally, the liposome's capacity to bind water may aid moisture retention conducive for tissue repair [Reimer et al., 2000].

Liposomes

Liposomes are spherical, lipid bilayer vesicles with a large aqueous inner-core for encapsulation and delivery of active agents [Park et al., 2005]. They can be composed of synthetic and/or natural phospholipids (e.g., phosphatidylcholine, PC) [Lonez et al., 2008; Sharma and Sharma, 1997; Pedrosa et al., 2010]. The structure of phospholipid molecules includes a hydrophilic head (polar) and a hydrophobic tail (non-polar). Upon hydration in an aqueous medium the polar region of the phospholipid orientates towards the aqueous medium, while the non-polar sites mutually attract and orientate inwards towards each other. The resultant liposome structure has a hydrophilic inner core encapsulating the aqueous medium and is surrounded by a phospholipid bilayer resembling biological cell membrane configuration [De Leeuw et al., 2009; Sharma and Sharma, 1997]. Membrane stabilizers such as sterol (e.g., cholesterol), proteins and lipid polymer conjugates can also be formulated into liposomes [Lian and Ho, 2001; Immordino et al., 2006].

During preparation, the most common liposomes formed are large multilamellar vesicles (LMVs) which have more than one bilayer and a diameter range of 0.5 - 10μm. Various post-formation modifications can be conducted to produce large unilamellar vesicles (LUVs, single bilayer, diameter 50-500nm) or small unilamellar vesicles (SUVs, single bilayer, diameter 25-50nm) [De Leeuw et al., 2009].

Liposomes can be tailored for site-specific delivery, for example, surface modifications by covalently binding polymers or attaching proteins, create liposomes that can be targeted to specific tissues (immunoliposomes). Alternatively, they can be formulated to avoid detection in the body for many hours thus dramatically reducing their clearance from the blood (stealth liposomes) [Gregoriadis, 1995]. The capacity to transport both hydrophilic and hydrophobic materials, has allowed a wide range of pharmaceutical formulations to be incorporated into liposome vesicles.

In terms of encapsulation, agents with varying lipophilicities can be sequestered either within the phospholipid bilayer (hydrophobic), entrapped in the inner core (hydrophilic), as well as in the inner and outer bilayer interface (hydrophilic) of the liposome [Sharma and Sharma, 1997]. Liposome encapsulation allows the potential of a controlled release delivery system to achieve effective drug delivery whilst reducing problems related to targeted delivery, biodistribution and bioavailability of agents, especially when administering cytotoxic agents [De Leeuw et al., 2009; Sharma and Sharma, 1997].

LIPOSOMAL DELIVERY OF ANTIBIOTICS

Fluoroquinolones

Ofloxacin is a second generation quinolone, which inhibits normal bacterial cell division by binding to DNA gyrase and type IV topoisomerase [Ofloxacin, Drug Bank Website; Rasool et al., 2010]. Ofloxacin shows extended activity against Gram-negative microorganisms, especially against

Gram-negative bacilli, but has limited activity against Gram-positive microorganisms. This antibiotic can be administered orally and intravenously for the treatment of diseases including respiratory tract, kidney, skin, soft tissue as well as urinary tract infection [Oliphant and Green, 2002]. Furneri et al. (2000) reported the development of unilamellar liposomes loaded with the fluoroquinolone antibiotic ofloxacin, and their *in vitro* activity against several strains of *Enterococcus faecalis, Escherichia coli, S. aureus* and *P. aeruginosa*. Minimum inhibitory concentration (MIC) values were compared for free and liposome encapsulated ofloxacin using a range of formulations (all 4:3:4 molar ratio): DMPC:CH:DP, DMPC:CH:DPPS, DMPC:CH:PE and DMPC:CH:PA (where DMPC = 1,2-dimyristoyl-*sn*-glycero-phosphocholine; CH = cholesterol; DP = dihexadecyl hydrogen phosphate; DPPS = dipalmitoyl-DL-α-phosphatidyl-L-serine; PE = 1,2-dimyristoyl-*sn*-glycero-phosphoethanolamine; PS = phosphatidylserine and PA = 1,2-dimyristoyl-*sn*-glycero-phosphatidic acid, sodium salt). In the majority of cases, the MIC of liposome encapsulated drug was at least two fold lower than that of free drug, with DMPC:CH:PA and DMPC:CH:DP showing the greatest enhancement of antimicrobial activity. Accumulation of a fixed concentration of drug (from both free and DMPC:CH:DP liposome encapsulated) was examined within *E. coli* (ATCC 25922, ATCC 35218) and *P. aeruginosa* (ATCC 27853) over 500 and 1500 seconds, respectively. For both species, drug entry into the cells started slowly before entering a rapid phase of uptake; liposomal ofloxacin reached significantly higher concentrations ($p < 0.001$) compared to free drug, indicating the vesicles enhanced interactions with bacteria. Taken together, these two results (decreased MIC with enhanced antimicrobial activity and increased bacterial uptake for liposome encapsulated drug) may result from the improved interactions between liposomes and bacteria most likely as a result of electrostatic interactions and or inclusion of fusogenic lipids in the formulation. The authors also concluded that liposomal delivery may be able to improve drug delivery to the mononuclear phagocytic system after systemic administration due to protection from harsh environmental conditions.

Similar to ofloxacin, ciprofloxacin is also a second generation quinolone that impairs bacterial cell replication by binding to DNA gyrase and topoisomerase IV [Ciprofloxacin, Drug Bank Website; Hawkey, 2003]. Ciprofloxacin can be administered orally or intravenously for treatment of a range of Gram-positive and Gram-negative bacteria, including *P. aeruginosa* [Oliphant and Green, 2002; Lee et al., 2010]. The use of sterically stabilised (polyethylene glycol conjugated to distearoyl phosphatidylethanolamine) liposomal ciprofloxacin delivery for treatment of pneumococcal pneumonia in rats infected with *Streptococcus pneumoniae* was reported by Ellbogen et al. (2003). Intravenously administered, sterically stabilised liposomal ciprofloxacin (40 or 80 mg/kg) was compared with free (conventional) ciprofloxacin (40 or 80 mg/kg) and ceftriaxone (an expanded spectrum cephalosporin approved for the treatment of pneumococcal infections, dosed at 100 mg/kg). Sterically stabilised liposomal ciprofloxacin produced the highest concentrations of drug in serum and lung lavage fluid, but disappointingly, survival rates were similar to those seen with administration of free drug, regardless of whether the dose was administered once or twice daily. Each therapy group was dosed for three days (18 h post intratracheal *S. pneumoniae* infection) and mortality observed for 10 days post infection. The survival rate for ceftriaxone was 100% over the 10 days of the study for both once and twice daily doses of drug. Survival rates were better for both forms of ciprofloxacin dosed twice daily, with the best outcome seen for free and sterically stabilised liposomal drug (80% survival at 10 days). The authors pointed out that whilst sterically stabilised liposomal ciprofloxacin resulted in higher concentrations of the drug in serum and lung lavage fluid, this may indicate an accumulation of entrapped rather than bioactive drug. There may also be issues with a lack of specific activity of ciprofloxacin against *S. pneumoniae* compared to other pneumonia-causing bacteria, e.g., *Klebsiella pneumoniae*.

Aminoglycosides

Neomycin is a topical and ophthalmic antibiotic which binds to a conserved sequence in the 16S ribosomal subunit [Fourmy et al., 1998; Neomycin, Drug Bank website]. Such interaction results in mRNA being misread, interferes with the normal protein synthesis and disintegration of polysomes occurs to produce non-functional monosomes [Neomycin, Drug Bank website]. Neomycin can generally be used for the treatment of infections caused by aerobic Gram-negative bacteria such as *Pseudomonas*, *Acinetobacter* and *Enterobacter* spp. Neomycin sulphate was formulated into elastic liposomes and applied to the treatment of deep dermal *S. aureus* infection in rats [Darwhekar et al., 2012]. Elastic liposomes differ from conventional liposomes in that they are highly deformable due to the inclusion of an edge-activator species (Tween® or Span®) in the phospholipid bilayer. They also have the added benefit of being able to permeate through the stratum corneum *via* the osmotic forces generated by the structure of the skin.

Elastic liposomal neomycin sulphate formulations were prepared from varying ratios of PC and 5 % w/w Tween 80 or Span 80 (95:5, 90:10, 85:15, 80:20, 75:25 % w/w). As the percentage of Tween® or Span® increased in the elastic liposome formulations, vesicle size reduced from 215 ± 2.1 nm and 223.2 ± 1.2 nm to 99.2 ± 1.1 nm and 118.3 ± 1.8 nm, respectively. Formulations containing PC:Surfactant 80:20 and 75:25 % w/w showed greatly diminished encapsulation efficiencies for neomycin sulphate: e.g., 32.4 ± 0.2 % versus 2.2 ± 0.2 % for PC: Tween 80 90:10 and 75:25 % w/w, respectively. When stored at 2 – 8 °C elastic liposome suspensions were found to be stable for up to 14 days compared to 2 months when vesicles were encapsulated in a Carbopol® gel. Drug loaded elastic liposomes were able to penetrate the dermis up to 180 µm in shaved rats and more importantly, when used to treat deep dermal infection caused by *S. aureus,* lead to both inhibition and eradication of the bacteria within 7 days. The authors concluded that this type of liposomal system could be a promising alternative for topical antibiotic drug delivery for treatment of deep dermal infections.

Cephalosporins

Ceftazidime is a semisynthetic derivative of the antibiotic cephaloridine, and is often used in the treatment of *Pseudomonas* spp. and other Gram-negative bacterial infections [Ceftazidime, Drug Bank website; PubChem Compound website]. Ceftazidime is administered intravenously or *via* the intramuscular route for the treatment of bacterial septicaemia and a range of infections, including lower respiratory tract, skin, urinary tract, bone, joint, gynaecological, intra-abdominal and central nervous infections [Ceftazidime, Drug Bank website]. The mechanism of action of ceftazidime is derived from its affinity for penicillin-binding proteins (PBPs) which enable the inhibition of functional enzymes responsible for cell wall synthesis [Ceftazidime, Drug Bank website]. Cefepime is a semi-synthetic, fourth generation cephalosporin which has the ability to rapidly penetrate into Gram-negative bacteria, has multiple PBPs targets and is resistant to inactivation by ß-lactamases [Cefepime, Drug Bank website; Sanders et al., 1996]. Cefepime has extended activity on both Gram-positive (including methicillin-sensitive *S. aureus* and *S. pneumoniae*) and Gram-negative bacteria (*E. coli, P. aeruginosa*, *K. pneumoniae* and *Enterobacteriaceae* spp.) with enhanced activity against those producing extended spectrum ß-lactamases [Cefepime, Drug Bank website; Yahav et al., 2007]. This intravenously administered antibiotic functions by disrupting the bacterial cell wall synthesis pathway [Cefepime, Drug Bank website]. Torres et al. (2012) reported the encapsulation of two cephalosporins, ceftazidime and cefepime, in PC:CH:α-tocopherol 40:10:0.04 or 40:20:0.04 molar ratio, and subsequent *in vitro* antimicrobial activity against two strains of *P. aeruginosa* (ATCC 27853 and SPM-1). Unilamellar liposomes with average diameter 131.88 nm had encapsulation efficiencies of 2.29% and 5.77% for cefepime and ceftazidime, respectively. Liposome stability (percentage drug release after 24 hours at 4 °C) was increased by increasing the molar ratio of CH to 50% for both drugs: Cefepime release was 97.19% and 44.91%, with ceftazidime release 98.25% and 63.25% for 25% and 50% CH, respectively. The cholesterol content was sufficiently high to ameliorate the membrane phase transition and substantially reduce membrane fluidity, thus increasing formulation stability and retention of the encapsulated drug. Antimicrobial efficacy for the two drugs also varied depending on whether they were delivered as free drug or in liposome-encapsulated form. The MIC for free cefepime and ceftazidime against *P. aeruginosa* ATC 27853 was 8 μg/mL while the value for liposomal drug fell to 4 μg/mL; MIC for ceftazidime against *P. aeruginosa* SPM-1 was 1024 μg/mL and 512 μg/mL for free and liposomal drug, respectively. This 50 % decrease in the MIC of liposomal versus free drug indicates that liposomal encapsulation is able to increase the antibacterial activity of these two drugs, probably *via* a liposome-bacterial cell enhanced fusion interaction.

Cefoxitin is a second generation semi-synthetic cephalosporin used in the treatment of infections caused by obligate or facultative intracellular microorganisms [Wallick and Hendlin, 1974], which is predominantly administered intravenously. The bactericidal activity of cefoxitin comes from its ability to inhibit cell wall synthesis in a broad range of aerobic and anaerobic Gram-negative bacteria, including *E. coli*, *Proteus mirabilis*, indole-positive *Proteus* and *Serratia* strains [Wallick and Hendlin, 1974; Cefoxitin, Drug Bank website]. Wu et al. (2004) investigated the biodistribution of cefotoxin-loaded liposomes by assessing organ distribution and transport into bile in rats. Having optimised drug-loaded formulations and preparation methods, liposomes prepared from DMPC:CH (2:1 molar ratio) were injected intravenously into male Wistar rats that had been fasted for 24 h. Blood samples and organs (liver, spleen, pancreas and kidneys) were harvested 1, 3 and 5 h after dosing; bile samples were also extracted 0.5, 1, 2, 3, 4, 5 and 5.5 h after an intravenous bolus delivered into the tail vein. Both the concentration and retention duration of drug in various organs were higher from liposomal cefoxitin, compared to free drug; the accumulation of liposomal cefoxitin in the pancreas also indicates that this form may be suitable for the treatment of acute pancreatitis. Liposomal cefoxitin drug concentration in bile was around 2.7 times higher than free drug 0.5, 1 and 2 h after administration. This may be explained by the fact that injected liposomes are preferentially taken up by organs of the reticuloendothelial system (RES), e.g., hepatic Kupffer cells and splenic macrophages, hence the administered dose is rapidly trafficked to the liver and bile.

Glycopeptides

Vancomycin is a branched, tricyclic glycosylated non-ribosomal peptide which exists with as an asymmetric dimer with the C-terminus D-Ala-D-Ala binding site arranged in opposite direction [Vancomycin, Drug Bank website; Muppidi et al. 2012]. This terminal binds to the polymeric lipid-PP-disaccharide-pentapeptides to disrupt the cross-linking of peptidoglycans during cell wall synthesis, hence weakening the bacterial cell structure [Schäfer et al., 1996]. This antibiotic is mainly administered orally or intravenously for the treatment of Gram-positive bacteria (*Staphylococcal* and *Streptococcal* spp.) [Vancomycin, Drug Bank website; Schäfer et al., 1996]. Nicolosi et al. (2010) investigated the use of fusogenic liposomes (i.e., liposomes that preferentially fuse with cell and other bilayer membranes) for *in vitro* delivery of vancomycin to a range of Gram-negative bacteria including *E. coli* (wild strains and ATCC 25922 as control), *K. pneumoniae, P. aeruginosa* (wild strains and ATCC 27853 as control) and *Acinetobacter baumannii.* Fusogenic liposomes were formulated from DOPE (dioleoylphosphatidylethanolamine): DPPC (dipalmitoylphosphatidyl-choline):CHEMS (cholesterol hemisuccinate) (4:2:4 molar ratio) and their MIC compared against free vancomycin (> 512 mg/L for all bacteria tested). Fusogenic liposomal vancomycin displayed dramatically reduced MIC ranges for both wild strain and control bacteria (where relevant): *E. coli* (wild strain) 6 – 25 mg/L, *E. coli* (ATCC 25922) 10.5 mg/L, *K. pneumoniae* 25 – 50 mg/L, *P. aeruginosa* wild strain 50 mg/L, *P. aeruginosa* (ATCC 27853) 83.7 mg/L and *Acinetobacter baumannii* 6 – 12.5 mg/L. Using SEM (scanning electron microscopy) and TEM (transmission electron microscopy) analysis of *E. coli* incubated with drug loaded DOPE:DPPC:CHEMS liposomes, the authors showed that not only do the liposome adhere to the bacteria, but in some cases ultrastructural modifications after vesicle fusion were visible. Detailed TEM images of the multi-layered cell envelope revealed that larger liposomes were able to fuse with the bacterial outer membrane and induce subsequent distortion and deformation of the structure. These alterations in structure were not seen when empty fusogenic liposomes were incubated with *E. coli* further supporting the assumption that the physical changes seen were the result of antimicrobial vancomycin activity.

Sande et al. (2012) recently reported the development of liposomal vancomycin formulations with the aim of improving its antistaphylococcal activity against methicillin-resistant *S. aureus* (MRSA). Two liposomal vancomycin formulations were developed: DSPC (1,2-distearoyl-*sn*-glycero-3-phosphocholine):DCP (dicetylphosphate):CH (7:2:1) and DSPC:DMPG (dimyristoylphosphatidylglycerol):CH (7:2:1) which produced 527.6 ± 58.2 nm sized liposomes with encapsulation efficiencies of 9 % and 20 % respectively. In terms of their *in vitro* antimicrobial efficacy, the MIC for DSPC:DCP:CH and DSPC:DMPG:CH liposomes was reduced for community-associated and hospital-associated MRSA strains by 2 and 4 fold relative to free drug; MBC values for both formulations were 4 fold lower than free drug. Treatment of *in vivo* MRSA infection in mice following an intraperitoneal injection of 3.9×10^6 CFU with 50 mg/mg DSPC:DCP:CH liposomal vancomycin administered one hour post infection was also investigated. Twenty four hours after liposomal vancomycin was administered, the mice were sacrificed to allow their spleen and kidneys to be removed and assessed for bacterial load. Compared to a phosphate buffered saline (PBS) solution control group, liposomal vancomycin reduced the bacterial load in the spleen and kidneys by 2 – 3 log CFU; compared to free vancomycin, the liposomal formulation was only able to affect a 1 log CFU reduction. The authors proposed that liposomal vancomycin had two major advantages over free drug: Firstly, liposome encapsulated vancomycin appears to enhance the uptake of drug possibly by fusing with the bacterial cell wall. Although the major targets of vancomycin are the terminal D-alanyl-D-alanine moieties of the NAM/NAG-peptides on the bacterial surface, liposomal delivery may facilitate binding to these groups before the drug is delivered across the cell membrane. The second advantage for liposome encapsulated vancomycin is that it appears able to reduce nephrotoxicity associated with the drug and can also facilitate delivery to selected tissues.

Pumerantz and co-workers recently published a series of reported on the development of PEGylated liposomes for vancomycin delivery to the lungs for treatment of MRSA pneumonia [Muppidi et al., 2011; Pumerantz et al., 2011; Muppidi et al., 2012]. Vancomycin was formulated into liposomes composed on DSPC:CH:MPEG-2000-DSPE (methylpolyethyleneglycol-1,2-distearoyl-phosphatidyl ethanolamine conjugate) (3:1:0.02 molar ratio) with a mean diameter of 245 ± 139 nm and 13 ± 3 % encapsulation efficiency. When compared against conventional liposomes (DSPC:CH, 3:1 molar ratio) the uptake of PEGylated vancomycin loaded vesicles into MRSA infected macrophages was greatly reduced. Whilst a sufficiently high, antimicrobial intracellular concentration of drug could be achieved with conventional liposomes, no effect on MRSA survival was observed for the DSPC:CH:MPEG-2000-DSPE formulation. The authors suggested that this effect was due to the stealth PEG component of the formulation which delayed phagocytosis into infected macrophages. *In vivo* biodistribution studies however, revealed that PEGylated liposomal vancomycin had prolonged blood circulation time (compared to conventional liposomes) and also showed increased deposition in the lungs, liver and spleen with a concurrent reduction in kidney accumulation. This interesting finding suggests that whilst stealth liposomal formulations may be limit the nephrotoxicity of vancomycin, and increase drug deposition in infected tissues (i.e., lungs in the case of MRSA pneumonia), there are still issues with targeting to infected macrophages. Using PEGylated, stealth liposomes as a depot in infected organs to increase localised drug concentration, rather than as a macrophage targeting system may be an alternative therapeutic approach in the treatment of MRSA pneumonia, especially in patients with impaired renal function.

Macrolides

Clarithromycin is a semi-synthetic macrolide derived from the 14-membered ring antibiotic, erythromycin [Gaynor and Mankin, 2003]. The activity of clarithromycin comes from its ability to bind to the 50S ribosomal subunit, thereby inhibiting peptidyl transferase activity which leads to the inhibition of bacterial protein synthesis [Clarithromycin, Drug Bank website]. This antibiotic is orally administered with known activity against many Gram-positive (*S. aureus, S. pneumoniae, and Streptococcus pyogenes*) and Gram-negative aerobic bacteria (including *Haemophilus influenzae, H. parainfluenzae, and Moraxella catarrhalis*) [Clarithromycin, Drug Bank website]. To develop a high dose, injectable formulation of clarithromycin, liposomes were formulated with 5:1 weight ratio PC:sodium cholesterol sulphate (SCS) with 0.2 – 0.5 % w/w *n*-hexyl acid [Liu et al., 2013]. Currently marketed injectable forms of clarithromycin are available as the lactobionate salt which has issues with high discontinuation rates and poor patient compliance. These issues arise from the high instance of phlebitis and inflammation at the infusion site resulting from the rapid, intimate contact of the formulation with vascular surfaces. A range of fatty acids were examined by the authors for their effect on encapsulation efficiency and vesicle characteristics; the final fatty acid chosen was found to not only improve the aqueous solubility of the drug but also increase its remote loading into liposomes and hence encapsulation efficiency. To improve stability of the clarithromycin loaded liposomes, a formulation screen of cryoprotectants was conducted to decrease encapsulated drug leakage, vesicle aggregation and hydrolysis of phospholipids. Of all the additives tested (5 – 15 % trehalose, glucose, sucrose, mannitol and blends of sucrose with glucose or mannitol), sucrose was found to be the most effective in this formulation by maintaining vesicle diameter to < 200 nm and preserving encapsulation efficiency of clarithromycin. *In vitro* release indicated that the process was biphasic, with initial burst release in the first 2 h, followed by slow prolonged release profile for the next 22 h. Finally, in order to assess whether these liposomal formulations were less irritant that the existing clarithromycin formulation, three animal models, namely the mouse scratch, rat paw lick and rabbit ear vein irritation tests, were explored. Briefly, the mouse scratch test comprises administering a subcutaneous injection of the intended dose and then observing the i) number of mice scratching within 15 min of dose administration (%), ii) average onset time for scratching to occur, and iii) average number of scratches each mouse makes within 15 min of the dose being administered. The rat paw lick involves injecting a single injection into the foot pad of the right hind paw and then observing the i) onset of paw licking and ii) the number of times the paw is licked in 15 min. Finally, the rabbit ear vein irritation test requires the specific dose of sample to be injected into the marginal ear veins at a constant rate (2 mL/min) for 3 consecutive days. A visual observation of the vascular reaction is recorded each day and one hour after the final dose is administered rabbit are sacrificed and vascular tissue at and near the injection site is removed for histopathological examination. All three of these *in vivo* tests revealed that the liposome encapsulated clarithromycin formulation was significantly less irritant. In the case of the mouse scratch test, not only did less individual mice scratch after the dose was administered (83% versus 100%) but the onset time for scratching to occur was also greatly reduced (128 s versus 52 s) compared to free drug. Similarly, for the rat paw lick test, both the onset and number of licks was significantly reduced for liposome encapsulated clarithromycin versus free drug. Interestingly, the rabbit ear vein irritation test revealed that whilst administration of free drug resulted in significant vascular discolouration, hyperemia and inflammatory cell infiltration, it was much less in evidence for liposomal clarithromycin. Overall, not only was liposome encapsulated clarithromycin a more stable formulation, but it was also shown in three different *in vivo* models to result in significantly less discomfort, irritation and inflammation at the site of injection.

Penicillins

A derivative of penicillin, ticarcillin is a semi-synthetic antibiotic with broad spectrum activity against a range of Gram-positive and Gram-negative bacteria, excluding those that produce β-lactamases. Ticarcillin's mechanism of action is the prevention of peptidoglycan crosslinking during cell wall synthesis as the microorganisms try to divide which ultimately results in bacterial cell death [Ticarcillin, Drug Bank website]. Gharib et al. (2012) recently reported on the *in vivo* and *in vitro* activity of a variety of ticarcillin-loaded liposome formulations against *P. aeruginosa* (ATCC 29248). Neutral (PC:CH 4:1 molar ratio), cationic (PC:CH:SA (stearylamine) 4:1:1 molar ratio) and anionic (PC:CH:DCP 4:1:1 molar ratio) liposomes all had a mean particle size of < 100 nm and encapsulation efficiency of 55 ± 0.21 %, 76 ± 0.17 % and 43 ± 0.14 %, respectively. Both neutral and cationic liposomal ticarcillin showed improved antimicrobial activity by four-fold and eight-fold decreases in MIC (mg/L) compared to free drug; anionic liposomes however showed a doubled MIC compared to free drug, which may result from a bacteria-vesicle steric repulsion effect. Using a murine *P. aeruginosa* infected thermal injury model, the authors showed that topical treatment with 1 mg/kg cationic liposomal ticarcillin (dosed for 7 days starting 3 days post-infection), a 100 % survival rate could be achieved. This compared favourably to the other modes of treatment where neutral liposomal, anionic liposomal and free drug resulted in 60, 20 and 30 % survival rates, respectively. Another interesting finding from this study was that no bacteria could be detected in the liver, spleen or skin for cationic liposomal ticarcillin animals; 1.013 ± 0.07 log CFU/g *P. aeruginosa* was detected in the kidney however. These promising results indicate that not only could infection at the burn site be controlled effectively by cationic liposomal ticarcillin, but it could also greatly reduce systemic bacterial dissemination to the organs.

Tetracyclines

Whilst tetracyclines are predominantly used as antibiotics in their own right, one member of the group, minocycline, also displays potent anti-inflammatory activity which could be useful in the treatment of acute and chronic wounds. Minocycline is a second generation derivative of tetracycline which is often administered orally [Ochsendorf, 2010]. This semi-synthetic compound has been chemically adapted to provide additional benefits, which includes having a longer half-life and higher lipophilicity resulting in better absorption in the intestines [Garner et al., 2003; Ochsendorf, 2010]. Similar to first generation tetracyclines, the mechanism of minocycline is also derived from its ability to inhibit bacterial protein synthesis. Minocycline has been found to be effective against a range of Gram-positive (e.g., *Streptococcus* spp., β-haemolytic streptococci) and Gram-negative (e.g., *Neisseria gonorrhoeae*, *H. influenzae*) bacteria [Ochsendorf, 2010]. In addition to the antimicrobial action, minocycline has also been used for the treatment of arthritis, pulmonary inflammation and neurodegenerative diseases, due to its anti-inflammatory, anti-apoptotic, anti-oxidant and neuroprotective properties [Plane et al., 2010; Ochsendorf, 2010]. In eukaryotes, molecular targets of minocycline include matrix mtelloproteinase-9 (MMP-9), vascular endothelial growth factor A, cytochrome c, interleukin-1β, arachidonate 5-lipozygenase, caspase 1 and 3 [Kaiser et al., 2013; Hu et al., 2009]. Kaiser et al. (2013) recently reported on the application of liposomal minocycline as a potential treatment for diabetic retinopathy, a chronic degenerative disease that can lead to blindness. Systemic minocycline therapy has previously been shown to reduce pro-inflammatory cytokine and caspase 3 expression in rat with experimentally induced diabetic retinopathy. The authors of this study prepared PC:DHP (dihexadecylphosphate):cholesterol (7:2:1) nanoliposomes (80 ± 20 nm) to deliver encapsulated minocycline *via* a subconjunctival injection. Their results showed that shortly after the injection, minocycline-loaded liposomes delivered a higher concentration of the drug to the retina and in a more sustained manner compared to free minocycline. Drug-loaded liposomes were most likely transported intact to the various regions of the eye (e.g., retina, lens, cornea), thereby increasing the concentration of minocycline delivered to the retina. Both free and liposomal minocycline had a measurable effect on several pro-inflammatory markers, with encapsulated drug affecting Lama5 and Icam1 gene targets by returning their expression to non-diabetic levels. In addition, liposomal minocycline also returned STAT3 (inflammatory mediator in the retina) and annexin V (involved in calcium ion transport) protein expression to pre-diabetic levels, indicating the anti-inflammatory potential of encapsulated drug in the treatment of diabetic retinopathy. The authors concluded however, that the selective effect of both free and liposomal minocycline on certain pro-inflammatory markers indicates that dosage and duration of treatment may need to be optimised further to improve therapeutic efficacy.

Others

Metronidazole

Metronidazole is a synthetic, nitroimidazole oral antibiotic, which is indicated for the treatment of anaerobic bacterial and protozoal infections as well as *Helicobacter pylori* eradication [BNF website]. Delivered as a prodrug, unionised metronidazole shows selective activity against anaerobes and protozoa because of their intracellular reduction of the drug to its active form. Metronidazole's mechanism of action involves covalent binding to microbial DNA, and subsequent inhibition of nucleic acid and protein synthesis [Metronidazole, Drug Bank website]. Vyas et al. (2007) described the development of mannosylated liposomes for metronidazole delivery to *S. aureus* biofilms both *in vitro* and *in vivo*. Egg PC:CH:SA (7:2:1 molar ratio) liposomes were coated with hydrophobised cholesteryl (CHM) or sialo- (SM) mannan derivatives to produce vesicles of 454 ± 42 nm and 467 ± 51 nm diameter, with 31.7 ± 2.5 and 30.9 ± 3.1% metronidazole entrapment, respectively. *In vitro* assessment revealed that SM-liposomes could achieve 97.9 ± 6.1% bacterial growth inhibition against a *S. aureus* biofilm, compared to 86.3 ± 4.5% for CHM-liposomes. Using an *S. aureus* pouch infection model in rats, SM-liposomes displayed a >3 log reduction (CFU/mL) whereas CHM-liposomes produced ≈ 2 log reduction, and both were significantly greater than free drug (<1 log reduction). The authors suggested that liposome encapsulation of metronidazole not only provides protection from β-lactamases and exogenous enzymes, but is also able to maintain a localised, high concentration of the drug at the site of activity. In addition, mannosylation of these liposomes acts as a targeting ligand to the biofilm *via* hydrogen bonding of the polyhydroxyl –OH terminal groups with monosaccharides of the bacterial glycocalyx. This target binding may also explain the fusogenic behaviour of mannosylated liposomes, which further enhances their ability to deliver efficiently an antibiotic directly to the biofilm.

Liposomal encapsulation of metronidazole is not without its difficulties however. Bardonnet et al. (2008) explored the issues associated with effective loading of metronidazole and ampicillin into a range of liposome formulations and their *in vitro* antimicrobial efficacy against *H. pylori*. Formulations based on DPPC and CH were examined, in addition to those containing a glycolipid cholesteryl tetraethyleneglycol fucose (Fuc-E_4-Chol) and Epikuron™ 170, a phospholipid-fatty acid mixture composed of >72% PC, >10% PE, <3% phosphatidylinositol (PI), <4% lyso-phosphatidylcholine (LPC) and ≈10% free fatty acids. Encapsulation efficiency varied dramatically between the formulations investigated:

- DPPC:CH (80:20): 11.2 ± 2.6% metronidazole; 10.0 ± 4.0% ampicillin
- Epikuron™ 170:CH (80:20): 1.4 ± 1.1% metronidazole; 13.9 ± 1.0% ampicillin
- DPPC:Fuc-E_4-Chol:CH (80:10:10): 13.0% metronidazole; 4.8% ampicillin (note only one measurement was taken for this sample)

The authors proposed that this difference in encapsulation efficiency may result from; 1) the location of metronidazole within the liposome structure; 2) diffusibility of the drug, and/or 3) liposome bilayer phase. The octanol/ water partition coefficient of metronidazole is -0.02, indicating that is most probably resides at the interface between the lipid bilayer and internal aqueous phase of the liposome. In addition, compared to ampicillin, metronidazole molecules are smaller and hence have greater potential for diffusion through the bilayer. Finally, X-ray diffraction studies have shown that when hydrated, Epikuron™ is present in the fluid state at 20°C which would substantially increase membrane permeability and therefore leakage of encapsulated materials. It is this latter physical state, combined with the properties of metronidazole, which most likely resulted in the dramatic difference between its encapsulation efficiency in DPPC:CH liposomes compared to the Epikuron™ formulation. At the same temperature, DPPC formulations would be in the gel state which is much less fluid and structured, with reduced permeability and leakage of encapsulated materials. The authors also reported that interactions between the various liposome formulations and two strains of *H. pylori* (reference and clinical strain) were dependent on several factors: *H. pylori* has an affinity for cholesterol-containing formulations, and all liposomes examined contained at least a 10% molar ratio of the sterol. Liposome surface charge can also greatly affect interactions between the vesicles and negatively charged bacterial cells such as *H. pylori*; e.g., formulations containing Epikuron™ are much more electronegative than those based on DPPC and would therefore experience electrostatic repulsion when in close contact with *H. pylori*. Finally, liposomes containing the glycolipid Fuc-E_4-Chol showed enhanced interactions with reference strain *H. pylori* cells, which was absent for the clinical strain. Interestingly, the reference strain expresses the BabA2 gene, which codes for an outer membrane protein that is able to bind to the Lewis b histo-blood group antigen found on human gastric epithelial cells. The fucose portion of the glycolipid-containing liposome formulations was most likely able to bind specifically with this *H. pylori* strain's BabA2 adhesin thereby facilitating the interaction. This work raised several important formulation issues that must be considered when formulating antibiotics into phospholipid vesicles, namely the physicochemical properties of the drug, the physical behaviour of the liposome formulation chosen and specific bacteria-environment interactions which can be used advantageously when designing drug delivery systems, e.g., interactions with fucose.

Polymyxin B

Polymyxins, such as polymyxin B and colistin, are polypeptide antibiotics with activity against a wide range of Gram-negative bacteria [Alipour et al., 2008]. The bactericidal action of polymyxins results from their cationic detergent activity and ability to bind to acidic groups in the bacterial cell membrane such as phospholipids and lipopolysaccharides, which results in leakage of vital cellular components and eventually death [Polymyxin B sulphate, Drug Bank website]. Use of the polymyxins today is generally restricted to treatment of infections caused by Gram-negative bacilli that are either resistant to other more common forms of treatment, or in patients who show intolerance to preferred antibiotic therapies [Alipour et al., 2008]. Alipour et al., (2008) described the development of DPPC:CH and POPC (1-palmitoyl-2-oleoyl-*sn*-glycero-3-phosphocholine):CH (both 2:1 molar ratio) liposome formulations for polymyxin B delivery to a range of Gram-negative microorganisms, including *Bordetella bronchiseptica, E. coli, K. pneumoniae, Acinetobacter lwoffii, Acinetobacter baumannii* and a range of *P. aeruginosa* clinical isolates. Reductions in bacterial counts with decreased MIC levels of polymyxin B were shown for all Gram-negative bacteria examined. The authors also showed higher penetration of liposomal polymyxin B into a resistant strain of *P. aeruginosa* (PA-M13641-1) compared to free drug.

More recently, He et al. (2013) described the enhanced efficacy of liposomal polymyxin B (compared to free drug) against a multidrug resistant

(MDR) clinical strain of *P. aeruginosa*. Drug-loaded DPPC:CH liposomes were used to deliver encapsulated polymyxin B to mice that had previously been infected with *P. aeruginosa via* the intratracheal route; the efficacy of liposomal drug was compared against free drug (both dosed at 3 mg/kg) and empty liposomes; all three treatment regimens were delivered intravenously every six hours. Mice were sacrificed 24 h after infection, and the lungs removed for quantitative culture analysis. At the start of the study (2 hours after intratracheal infection) mice had 3.1 – 3.6 $\log_{10}$ CFU/g for *P. aeruginosa* PA9019 (a clinical blood stream isolate) and 4.2 – 5.1 $\log_{10}$ CFU/g for *P. aeruginosa* PA27853 (a reference sample); after 24 hours, those mice in the control group who were treated with empty liposomes displayed increased bacterial burdens of 8.4 – 9.1 $\log_{10}$ CFU/g for PA9019 and 8.5 – 9.2 $\log_{10}$ CFU/g for PA27853. After 24 h treatment with liposomal polymyxin B, PA9019 infection was reduced to 3.8 ± 0.7 $\log_{10}$ CFU/g ($p<0.001$) with a similar profile observed for PA27853. Conversely, doses of the free drug were only able to achieve a minimal antimicrobial effect with results similar to those seen for empty liposomes. The authors reasoned that after intravenous administration, polymyxin B liposomes are taken up by macrophages in the lung, where drug is subsequently released into the epithelial lining fluid, thus resulting in higher drug concentrations at the site of infection.

Liposomal Delivery of Antifungals

Amphotericin B

Amphotericin B is a macrocyclic, polyene antibiotic which is biosynthesised by *Streptomyces nodosus*. In common with other antifungal drugs, amphotericin B exerts its activity by binding ergosterol, a sterol component of the fungal cell membrane, irreversibly altering membrane fluidity and leading to leakage of components and eventually cell death [AmBisome website]. Albasarah et al. (2010) characterised a chitosan coated liposomal system for the nebulised delivery of amphotericin B. The drug was encapsulated into PC liposomes with 0.9 % sodium chloride solution and various concentrations of chitosan chloride (0.1 – 0.3 % w/v). Using ethanol-based pro-liposomes, 80% encapsulation efficiency of amphotericin B could be achieved in the chitosan coated liposomes and after delivery *via* nebulisation, 60 % of the encapsulated drug was distributed in the lower stage of a two stage impinge. This later result indicates that this formulation would be capable of efficient drug delivery to the lower respiratory tract, where hard to treat pockets of infection reside. *In vitro* antifungal activity of chitosan coated liposomal amphotericin B revealed that the encapsulated drug could inhibit fungal growth to a similar extent as micellar amphotericin B; MIC values for coated liposomal amphotericin B and the micellar form against *C. albicans* and *Candida tropicalis* were all 0.5 μg/mL.

Liposomal amphotericin B has also been co-delivered into with terbinafine for the treatment of *Fusarium verticillioides*, a plant pathogen which can cause deep seated infections in humans [Ruíz-Cendoya et al., 2011]. In the clinic, fusariosis is generally treated with AmBisome (liposomal amphotericin B) or voriconazole chemotherapy, even though their efficacy in questionable. Combination treatments may be more effective however, such as liposomal amphotericin B combined with terbinafine (MIC range against *F. verticillioides* 0.125 – 1.0 mg/L). Using two clinical isolates of *F. verticillioides* (FMR 8585 AND FMR 9434) the authors assessed the *in vitro* and *in vivo* antifungal efficacy, including fungal load in spleen and kidneys, as well as survival rate in a murine model. *In vitro* antifungal activity revealed MIC values of 0.125 mg/L for terbinafine alone against both *F. verticillioides* strains and 2 mg/L (FMR 9434) and 4 mg/L (FMR 8585) for liposomal amphotericin B; interestingly, when the two drugs were combined their effect was found to be indifferent against both *F. verticillioides* strains. *In vivo* antifungal activity showed differing effects depending on the strain of *F. verticillioides* in question: Liposomal amphotericin B significantly reduced the fungal load (FMR 9434) in the spleen ($p < 0.005$) and kidneys (FMR 8585) ($p < 0.089$) compared to the control group (no treatment). When combined with terbinafine, the reduction in fungal load (compared to the control group) for both *F. verticillioides* strains was much more pronounced ($p < 0.035$ and 0.0001, respectively). Terbinafine alone did not significantly reduce the fungal burden in any organs tested. In terms of survival, all therapies improved the rates compared to the control group with combination liposomal amphotericin B and terbinafine showing greatest efficacy against FMR 9434 and liposomal amphotericin B alone most effective against FMR 8585. Taken together, these results suggest that combination chemotherapy may prove more effective against *F. verticillioides* in a clinical setting than the current recommended monotherapy.

Watanabe et al. (2010) described the deposition of liposomal amphotericin B in the lung of a patient suffering with pulmonary aspergillosis, and being treated for metastatic oesophageal cancer. In contrast to certain bacterial infections which reside either intracellularly or at vascular sites, fungal infections, such as those caused by *Aspergillus* spp. are manifest at extravascular sites within the airway. Following a resection of the lung, drug concentrations in both infected and uninfected tissue as well as that in plasma were assessed to determine where the delivered liposomal dose had accumulated. Amphotericin B concentrations were 5.2 times higher in the infected lesion than that circulating in blood plasma; drug concentration in uninfected lung tissue was 3.7 times higher than that in plasma. These results support the hypothesis that liposomal amphotericin B preferentially accumulates in infected lung lesions compared to either uninfected lung tissue or plasma; this effect may be the result of reticuloendothelial system (RES) saturation which allows accumulation at non-RES organs, *i.e.* lungs.

Nystatin

The potent antifungal agent nystatin is synthesised by *Streptomyces noursei* and acts by binding to sterols in the fungal cell membrane. It is active against a range of fungal infections including those caused by *Candida*, *Aspergillus* and *Fusarium* spp. [Church et al., 2006]. Nasti et al. (2006) reported on the application of pH-sensitive liposomes loaded with nystatin for treatment of *Cryptococcus neoformans* infection in a murine model. pH-sensitive liposomes (CHEMS:DOPE, 2:3 molar ratio) were compared to a conventional PC:CH (1:0.43) formulation; encapsulation efficiency for both liposomal formulations was high at 90 ± 4 % and 92 ±4 %, respectively. A murine model of *C. neoformans* was induced and effectiveness of pH-sensitive and conventional liposomal nystatin compared against free drug by assessing survival rates and fungal loads in liver and brain. Mice treated with pH-sensitive liposomal nystatin had an 80 % survival rate and a significantly lower fungal load in the liver and brain (Log_{10} cfu/organ) compared to the conventional liposomal formulation or free drug. This compares very favourably to mice treated with conventional liposomal nystatin and free drug whose survival rate was only 40 % and 20 % respectively. The anticryptococcal activity of pH-sensitive liposomes may result from pH – dependent release of drug in the macrophage's lysosome (low pH) which allows site specific intracellular targeting of the nystatin.

A wide ranging *in vitro* study by Johnson et al. (1998) reported the antifungal activity of unencapsulated, commercially available liposomal nystatin and four amphotericin B formulations. Two hundred isolates (including 162 clinical isolates) were screened as follows: 10 *Aspergillus flavus*, 30 *A. fumigatus*, 40 *C. albicans*, 20 *C. glabrata*, 10 *C. kefyr*, 20 *C. krusei*, 10 *C. lusitaniae*, 20 *C. parapsilosis*, 20 *C. tropicalis* and 20 *C. neoformans*. The antifungal products examined were as follows:

- Nyotran®: liposomal nystatin (DMPC:DMPG:nystatin, 7:3:1 molar ratio)
- Fungizone®: amphotericin B deoxycholate (sodium deoxycholate:amphotericin B, 4:5 molar ratio)
- AmBisome®: liposomal amphotericin B (HSPC (hydrogenated soya phophatidylcholine):CH:DSPG (distearoylphosphatidylglycerol): amphotericin B, 10:5:4:2 molar ratio)
- Amphocil®: amphotericin B colloidal dispersion (sodium cholesteryl sulphate: amphotericin B 1:1 molar ratio)
- Abelcet®: amphotericin B lipid complex (DMPC:DMPG: amphotericin B, 7:3:10 molar ratio)

In vitro antifungal activity was assessed by the broth microdilution method to determine minimum lethal concentration (MLC) and MIC values. Both free and liposomal nystatin showed fungistatic and fungicidal activities against the 10 species tested. Neither form of nystatin had the antifungal efficacy of Fungizone® or Abelcet®, but they were more effective than AmBisome®.

Carillo-Muñoz et al. (1999) conducted a similar *in vitro* screen as Johnson et al. (1998) to assess the susceptibility of 129 clinical isolates of yeast to liposomal nystatin as well as free nystatin, amphotericin B lipid complex, liposomal amphotericin B, amphotericin B cholesteryl sulphate, amphotericin B desoxycholate, fluconazole and itraconazole. The following species were examined: *C. albicans, C. parapsilosis, C. tropicalis, C. glabrata, C. krusei, C. guilliermondii, C. famata, C. kefyr, C. rugosa, C. viswanathii, Cryptococcus laurentii, C. neoformans, Rhodotorula rubra, Trichosporon* spp., as well as *C. krusei* ATCC 6258 and *C. parapsilosis* ATCC 22019 as quality control strains. The mean MIC values for all strains were found to be 0.96 mg/L for liposomal nystatin, 0.54 mg/L for free nystatin, 0.65 mg/L for amphotericin B lipid complex, 1.07 mg/L for liposomal amphotericin B, 0.75 mg/L for amphotericin B cholesteryl sulphate, 0.43 mg/L for amphotericin B desoxycholate, 5.53 mg/L for fluconazole and 0.33 mg/L for itraconazole. Two major findings from this work were firstly, that liposomal nystatin has greater antifungal activity than fluconazole and secondly, that all MIC levels were lower than those concentrations reported in blood samples after therapeutic doses had been administered.

Imidazoles

De Logu et al. (1997 and 2000) reported on the interactions between two imidazoles (miconazole and ketoconazole) and liposomes (PC:CH) including alterations in their antifungal activity. Ketoconazole and miconazole, both imidazole derivatives, display antifungal activity against the majority of pathogenic fungi and are also active against some Gram-positive bacteria [De Logu et al., 1997]. Examining their effects on *C. albicans* E10231 indicated that the source of phospholipids used to prepare the liposomes (i.e., egg or soy PC) had no effect on the antifungal activity of either miconazole or ketoconazole. Instead it was the concentration in which that phospholipid:drug combination was formulated which has the greatest effect on *in vitro* antifungal efficacy. Interestingly a difference was also seen depending on whether small unilamellar vesicles (SUV) or multilamellar vesicles (MLV) were used to encapsulate the drug, with MLV generally showing greater *in vitro* activity. Overall, SUV and MLV liposomal formulations of imidazoles showed less antifungal activity than free drug, which may be due to interactions between the drug and phospholipids. The authors also concluded that the inclusion of cholesterol in these formulations had no effect on antifungal activity unlike that seen with other antifungals, e.g., amphotericin B.

Tang et al. (2010) reported on variations in biodistribution and pharmacokinetics for itraconazole delivered to rats and mice as either liposomal (PC, CH and hyodeoxycholic acid sodium) or the commercially available Sporanox® inclusion complex (solubilised in hydroxypropyl-β-cyclodextrin (HP-β-CD)) formulations. Itraconazole is an azole which is available as an oral of intravenous formulation and has broad spectrum activity against *Aspergillus* spp. and *C. albicans* as well as other *Candida* spp. Itraconazole acts by interrupting the synthesis of ergosterol (a vital fungal cell membrane component). Two major advantages of itraconazole are that it is less nephrotoxic than amphotericin B and has a wider spectrum of activity than fluconazole. Formulation of itraconazole is not without difficulty however as its weakly basic nature leads to ionisation at low pH which can be problematic for orally delivered compounds. In addition the aqueous solubility of itraconazole is 1.8 μg/mL at pH 1.2, and it is highly lipophilic with an *n*-

octanol/water partition coefficient of 5.66 at physiological pH (8.1) [Tang et al., 2010]. Sporanox® is used in the treatment of severe fungal infections such as necrotising pneumonia and invasive pulmonary aspergillosis, but cannot be prescribed to patients with renal impairment due to both the toxicity of the drug and carrier system (HP-β-CD). Liposomes prepared in this study had an average diameter of 264.5 nm and entrapment efficiency was 73.82 ± 0.73 %. Biodistribution studies revealed major differences between the two forms of itraconazole, which were both administered intravenously (10 mg/kg). Whilst there was no difference between liposomal and HP-β-CD itraconazole distributed in the lungs, a much higher concentration of drug was found in the liver and spleen for liposomal drug. Conversely, low concentrations of drug were found in the heart and kidneys for liposomal itraconazole, which suggests that this mode of delivery could be useful for reducing toxicity seen in these organs.

LIPOSOMAL DELIVERY OF NATURAL PRODUCTS

Detoni et al. (2009) assessed the antimicrobial activity of the essential oil from *Zanthoxylum tingoassuiba* and also explored the possibility of encapsulating it into multilamellar liposomes. Classed as a medicinal plant in the Brazilian region, *Zanthoxylum tingoassuiba A.* St. Hill (Rutaceae) has been reported to possess anti-inflammatory, antibacterial and antifungal activity, possibly as a result of its high terpene and sesquiterpene content. The antibacterial and antifungal properties of *Z. tingoassuiba*'s essential oil were investigated by the disc diffusion method, and the physicochemical characteristics of a liposomal formulation were also explored. Essential oil loaded DPPC liposomes were found to have a smaller, less polydisperse mean diameter than empty DPPC liposomes: DPPC:Essential Oil (2.7:1 w/w) liposomes were 9.37 ± 4.69 μm and DPPC:Essential Oil (1.7:1 w/w) liposomes were 9.37 ± 4.06 μm, compared to 10.29 ± 8.21 μm for empty liposomes. Both essential oil loaded formulations had an encapsulation efficiency of 43.7 ± 6.0 %. The free essential oil was found to be active against dermatophyte fungi (e.g., *Trichophyton mentagrophytes, Epidermophyton floccosum* and *Microsporum gypseum*) and bacteria, including *S. aureus, Streptococcus mutans* and *Micrococcus luteus*. This activity was most likely due to the pinene, cineole, linalool and α-bisabolol components. The authors were unable to test the current liposome formulation for antimicrobial activity as the large size of the vesicles versus the size of the micro-organisms was found to be prohibitive.

Gortzi et al. (2007) reported on the antimicrobial activities before and after liposome encapsulation of two extracts (methanol or dichloromethane) of *Origanum dictamnus. O. dictamnus* is a native plant commonly found on the rocky mountains of Crete and has historically been used in wound healing amongst other applications. Liposomes prepared from PC:CH (5:1 w/w) were used to encapsulate the methanolic extract from *O. dictamnus*; two formulations were examined, namely one from a wild species and one from a cultivated species of *O. dictamnus*. Using a disc diffusion method to assess antimicrobial activity, liposome encapsulated *O. dictamnus* (wild) was effective against a range of wound infecting microorganisms including *S. aureus, P. aeruginosa, K. pneumoniae* and *C. albicans*. Antimicrobial activity was higher for liposome encapsulated essential oil than for the free form, indicating that the use of SUVs (275 ± 12 nm) for delivery could be an interesting prospect for the treatment of topical infections.

In addition to plant extract, other natural products including fatty acids and peptides have been investigated for their antimicrobial activity and potential for liposome encapsulation. Huang et al. (2011) recently reported the development of a liposomal formulation of oleic acid for treating MRSA skin infections. Several free fatty acids and their esters, found naturally in human skin, breast milk and the bloodstream, are known to possess antibacterial activity against Gram-positive species. Their mechanism of antimicrobial activity is thought to result from membrane disruption and an increase in membrane permeability. Fatty acid loaded liposomes were prepared from PC:CH:oleic acid (5:1:4 weight ratio) and could reduce MRSA 252 counts to undetectable levels at concentrations of 6.25 μg/mL and above; free oleic acid reduced the bacterial count to undetectable levels at a slightly higher concentration of 10 μg/mL. When tested *in vivo,* using a mouse skin lesion model, liposomal oleic acid reduced the bacterial counts (CFU) by more than 2.5 ($\log_{10}$CFU/mL) compared to treatment with empty liposomes. A further promising result to come from this study was that preliminary toxicity data indicated that liposomal oleic acid is biocompatible with normal tissues. On a similar theme, Kilian et al. (2011) described liposomal formulations of the cyclic dipeptide cyclo(L-tyrosyl-L-prolyl) (cyclo(Tyr-Pro)) and its antimicrobial activity (MIC) against a range of microorganisms. Using DPPC:CH (2:1 molar ratio) the MIC of liposome encapsulated cyclo(Tyr-Pro) was lower than free cyclic dipeptide for the following bacteria: *S. aureus, E. coli, K. pneumoniae* and *Bacillus subtilis*. The improvement in antimicrobial activity may be due to improved bacterial uptake of liposomes or protection of the cyclic dipeptide against enzymatic degradation. It is worth noting however, that no antimicrobial activity (for either the free or liposomal form) was seen for *C. albicans* or two MRSA strains.

Low et al. (2011 and 2013) reported on the antimicrobial efficacy of tea tree oil in combination with silver ions, both as free agents and as a liposome encapsulated formulation against typical wound infecting microorganisms *P. aeruginosa, S. aureus* and *C. albicans.* The antimicrobial activity of the tea tree oil-silver ion combination (versus single agents) could be seen at sub-minimal lethal concentrations, with a loss of microbial viability. Interestingly, the combination treatment against *P. aeruginosa* was synergistic, but indifferent against *S. aureus* and *C. albicans.* When encapsulated into liposomes (PC:CH 2:1 molar ratio) the minimum lethal concentrations (MLC) for tea tree oil were substantially reduced; the MLC value for liposomal silver ions remained the same as the free agent. Combining tea tree oil and silver in a liposomal formulation enhanced the antimicrobial activity against all three microorganisms. The authors suggested that liposome encapsulation may be able to reduce the incidence of side effects and also limit the development of resistance associated with single antimicrobial agents.

CONCLUSION

Infected wounds are a uniquely challenging environment for drug delivery due to their physical structure, the presence of exudate and necrotic material as well as their polymicrobial infection potential. Liposomes as drug delivery systems can effectively deliver antibiotics, antifungals and natural products to topical or disseminated systemic infections. Their phospholipid bilayer composition and controlled release behaviour makes liposomes amendable for delivery of antimicrobial agents to bacterial and fungal microbial communities alike, in spite of their widely differing morphology and physiology. The liposome's ability to carry hydrophilic and/or lipophilic materials also enhances and extends the range of materials they can deliver to sites of infection. In addition, accumulation at sites of infection such as the lungs, can be achieved by increasing liposome circulation times using stealth technologies such as PEGylation. In conclusion, as the molecular mechanisms underlying wound healing, inflammation and microbial infection are elucidated, these inevitably lead to the identification of new targets for drug delivery systems. Ultimately, it is these targets, combined with developments in novel, customised antimicrobials, which will lead to more efficacious liposome formulation strategies for wound therapies in the future.

REFERENCES

Albasarah, Y.Y., et al. (2010). Chitosan-coated antifungal formulations for nebulisation. *Journal of Pharmacy and Pharmacology*, 62, 821-828.

Alipour, M., et al. (2008). Antimicrobial effectiveness of liposomal polymyxin B against resistant Gram-negative bacterial strains. *International Journal of Pharmaceutics*, 355, 293-298.

AmBisome. Ambisome website [online]. 2013 [cited 31st October 2013]. Available from: http://www.ambisome.com.

Bardonnet, P-L., et al. (2008). Pre-formulation of liposomes against *Helicobacter pylori*: Characterisation and interaction with the bacteria. *European Journal of Pharmaceutics and Biopharmaceutics*, 69, 908-922.

BNF (British National Formulary) website. 5.1.11 Metronidazole and tinidazole. 2013 [cited 22nd October 2013]. Available from: http://www.medicinescomplete.com/mc/bnf/current/PHP3645-metronidazole-and-tinidazole.htm.

Bos, J.D. and Meinardi, M.M.H.M. (2000). The 500 Dalton rule for the skin penetration of chemical compounds and drugs. *Experimental Dermatology*, 9, 165-169.

Bowler, P.G., et al. (2001) Wound microbiology and associated approaches to wound management. *Clinical Microbiology Review*, 14, 244-269.

Carillo-Muñoz, A.J., et al. (1999). *In vitro* antifungal activity of liposomal nystatin in comparison with nystatin, amphotericin B cholesteryl sulphate, liposomal amphotericin B, amphotericin B lipid complex, amphotericin B desoxycholate, fluconazole and itraconazole. *Journal of Antimicrobial Chemotherapy*, 44, 397-401.

Cefepime. Drug Bank website [online]. 2013 [cited 28th October 2013]. Available from: http://www.drugbank.ca/drugs/DB01413.

Cefoxitin. Drug Bank website [online]. 2013 [cited 30th October 2013]. Available from: http://www.drugbank.ca/drugs/DB01331.

Ceftazidime. Drug Bank website [online]. 2013 [cited 28th October 2013]. Available from: http://www.drugbank.ca/drugs/DB00438.

Ceftazidime. PubChem Compound website [online]. 2013 [cited 28th October 2013]. Available from: http://pubchem.ncbi.nlm.nih.gov/summary/summary.cgi?cid=5484131&loc=ec_rcs

Church, D., et al. (2006). Burn wound infections. *Clinical Microbiology Reviews*, 19, 403-434.

Ciprofloxacin. Drug Bank website [online]. 2013 [cited 28th October 2013]. Available from: http://www.drugbank.ca/drugs/DB00537.

Clarithromycin. Drug Bank website [online]. 2013 [cited 30th October 2013]. Available from: http://www.drugbank.ca/drugs/DB01211.

Darwhekar, G., et al. (2012). Elastic liposomes for delivery of neomycin sulphate in deep skin infection. *Asian Journal of Pharmaceutical Sciences*, 7, 230-240.

De Leeuw, J., et al. (2009). Liposomes in dermatology today. *Journal of the European Academy of Dermatology and Venereology*, 23, 505-516.

De Logu, A., et al. (2000). Prevention by L-α-phosphatidylcholine of antifungal activity *in vitro* of liposome-encapsulated imidazoles determined by using time-killing curves. *International Journal of Antimicrobial Agents*, 15, 43-48.

De Logu, A., et al. (1997). Effects of *in vitro* activity of miconazole and ketoconazole in phospholipid formulations. *Journal of Antimicrobial Chemotherapy*, 40, 889-893.

Detoni, C.B., et al. (2009). Essential oil from *Zanthoxylum tingoassuiba* loaded into multilamellar liposomes useful as antimicrobial agents. *Journal of Microencapsulation*, 26, 684-691.

Drulis-Kawa, Z. and Dorotkiewicz-Jach, A. (2010). Liposomes as delivery systems for antibiotics. *International Journal of Pharmaceutics*, 387, 187-198.

Ellbogen, M.H., et al. (2003). Efficacy of liposome-encapsulated ciprofloxacin compared with ciprofloxacin and ceftriaxone in a rat model of pneumococcal pneumonia. *Journal of Antimicrobial Chemotherapy*, 51, 83-91.

Fonder, M.A., et al. (2008). Treating the chronic wound: A practical approach to the care of non-healing wounds and wound care dressings. *Journal of the American Academy of Dermatology*, 58, 185-206.

Fourmy, D., et al. (1998). Binding of neomycin-class aminoglycoside antibiotics to the A-site of 16 S rRNA. *Journal of Molecular Biology*, 277, 347-362.

Furneri, P.M., et al. (2000). Ofloxacin-loaded liposomes: *In Vitro* activity and drug accumulation in bacteria. *Antimicrobial Agents and Chemotherapy*, 44, 2458-2464.

Gallant-Behm, C.L., et al. (2005). Comparison of *in vitro* disc diffusion and time kill-kinetic assays for the evaluation of antimicrobial wound dressing efficacy. *Wound Repair and Regeneration*, 13, 412-421.

Garner, S.E., et al. (2003). Minocycline for acne vulgaris: Efficacy and safety. *Cochrane Database Systematic Reviews*, 1, CD002086.

Gaynor, M., & Mankin, A.S. (2003). Macrolide antibiotics: Binding site, mechanism of action, resistance. *Current Topics in Medicinal Chemistry*, 3, 949-960.

Gharib, A., et al. (2012). *In vitro* and *in vivo* activities of ticarcillin-loaded nanoliposomes with different surface charges against *Pseudomonas aeruginosa* (ATC 29248). *DARU Journal of Pharmaceutical Sciences*, 20, 41.

Gortzi, O., et al. (2007). Evaluation of the antimicrobial and antioxidant activities of *Origanum dictamnus* extracts before and after encapsulation in liposomes. *Molecules*, 12, 932-945.

Gregoriadis, G. (1995). Engineering liposomes for drug delivery: progress and problems. *Trends in Biotechnology*, 13, 527-537.

Gurtner, G.C., et al. (2008). Wound repair and regeneration. *Nature*, 453(7193), 314-321.

Hawkey, P.M. (2003). Mechanisms of quinolone action and microbial response. *Journal of Antimicrobial Chemotherapy*, 51, 29-35.

He, J. et al. (2013). Pharmacokinetics and efficacy of liposomal polymyxin B in a murine pneumonia model. *International Journal of Antimicrobial Agents*, http://dx.doi.org/10.1016/j.ijantimicag.2013.07.009.

Hu, W., et al. (2009). PEG minocycline-liposomes ameliorate CNS autoimmune disease. *PLoS ONE* 4: e4151. Doi:10.1371/journal.pone.0004151.

Huang, C-M., et al. (2011). Eradication of drug resistant *Staphylococcus aureus* by liposomal oleic acids. *Biomaterials*, 32, 214-221.

Immordino, M.L., et al. (2006). Stealth liposomes: review of the basic science, rationale, and clinical applications, existing and potential. *International Journal of Nanomedicine*, 1, 297-315.

Johnson, E.M., et al. (1998). Comparison of *in vitro* antifungal activities of free and liposome-encapsulated nystatin with those of four amphotericin B formulations. *Antimicrobial Agents and Chemotherapy*, 42, 1412-1416.

Kaiser, J.M., et al. (2013). Nanoliposomal minocycline for ocular drug delivery. Nanomedicine: *Nanotechnology, Biology and Medicine*, 9, 130-140.

Karande, P. and Mitragotri, S. (2009). Enhancement of transdermal drug delivery via synergistic action of chemicals. Biochimica et Biophysica Acta (BBA) - *Biomembranes*, 1788, 2362-2373.

Kilian, G., et al. (2011). Antimicrobial activity of liposome encapsulated cyclo(L-tyrosyl-L-prolyl). *Pharmazie*, 66, 421-423.

Lee, Y.J., et al. (2010). Fluoroquinolone resistance of *Pseudomonas aeruginosa* isolates causing nosocomial infection is correlated with levofloxacin but not ciprofloxacin use. *International Journal of Antimicrobial Agents*, 35, 261-264.

Lian, T. and Ho, R.J.Y. (2001). Trends and developments in liposome drug delivery systems. *Journal of Pharmaceutical Sciences*, 90, 667-680.

Liu, X., et al. (2013). Clarithromycin-loaded liposomes offering high drug loading and less irritation. *International Journal of Pharmaceutics*, 443, 318-327.

Lonez, C., et al. (2008). DiC14-amidine confers new anti-inflammatory properties to phospholipids. *Cellular and Molecular Life Sciences*, 65, 620-630.

Low, W. L., et al. (2013). Antimicrobial efficacy of liposome encapsulated silver ions and tea tree oil against *Pseudomonas aeruginosa, Staphylococcus aureus* and *Candida albicans. Letters in Applied Microbiology*, 57, 33-39.

Low, W.L., et al. (2011). Antimicrobial efficacy of silver ions in combination with tea tree oil against *Pseudomonas aeruginosa, Staphylococcus aureus* and *Candida albicans. International Journal of Antimicrobial Agents*, 37, 162-165.

Metronidazole. Drug Bank website [online]. 2013 [cited 22nd October 2013]. Available from: http://www.drugbank.ca/drugs/DB00916

Muppidi, K., et al. (2011). PEGylated liposome encapsulation increases the lung tissue concentration of vancomycin. *Antimicrobial Agents and Chemotherapy*, 55, 4537-4542.

Muppidi, K., et al. (2012). Development and stability studies of novel liposomal vancomycin formulations. *ISRN Pharmaceutics*, volume 2012, article ID 636743.

Mura, S., et al. (2009). Penetration enhancer-containing vesicles (PEVs) as carriers for cutaneous delivery of minoxidil. *International Journal of Pharmaceutics*, 380, 72-79.

Nasti, T.H., et al. (2006). Enhanced efficacy of pH-sensitive nystatin liposomes against *Cryptococcus neoformans* in murine model. *Journal of Antimicrobial Chemotherapy*, 57, 349-352.

Neomycin. Drug Bank website [online]. 2013 [cited 28th October 2013]. Available from: http://www.drugbank.ca/drugs/DB00994.

Nicolosi, D., et al. (2010). Encapsulation in fusogenic liposomes broadens the spectrum of action of vancomycin against Gram-negative bacteria. *International Journal of Antimicrobial Agents*, 35, 553-558.

Ochsendorf, F. (2010). Minocycline in Acne Vulgaris. *American Journal of Clinical Dermatology*, 11, 327-341.

Ofloxacin. Drug Bank website [online]. 2013 [cited 28th October 2013]. Available from: http://www.drugbank.ca/drugs/DB01165.

Oliphant C.M. and Green G.M. (2002). Quinolones: A comprehensive review. *American Family Physician*, 65: 455–464.

Ovington, L.G. (2007). Advances in wound dressings. *Clinics in Dermatology*, 25, 33-38.

Park, S.-H., et al. (2005). Effects of silver nanoparticles on the fluidity of bilayer in phospholipid liposome. *Colloids and Surfaces B: Biointerfaces*, 44, 117-122.

Pavelic, Z., et al. (2005). Characterisation and *in vitro* evaluation of bioadhesive liposome gels for local therapy of vaginitis. *International Journal of Pharmaceutics*, 301, 140-148.

Pedrosa, L., et al. (2010). Short-chain sphingolipids for enhanced cellular uptake of liposome-encapsulated amphiphilic anti-cancer drugs. *BMC Proceedings*, 4(Supplement 2), P39.

Plane, J.M., et al. (2010). Prospects for minocycline neuroprotection. *Archives of Neurology*, 67, 1442-1448.

Polymyxin B sulphate. Drug Bank website [online]. 2013 [cited 22nd October 2013]. Available from: http://www.drugbank.ca/drugs/DB00781.

Pumerantz, A. et al. (2011). Preparation of liposomal vancomycin and intracellular killing of methicillin-resistant *Staphylococcus aureus* (MRSA). *International Journal of Antimicrobial Agents*, 37, 140-144.

Rasool, F., et al. (2010). The effect of binders on the bioavailability of ofloxacin tablets in animal model. *Acta Poloniae Pharmaceutica*, 67, 185-189.

Reimer, K., et al. (2000). An innovative topical drug formulation for wound healing and infection treatment: *In vitro* and *in vivo* investigations of a povidone-iodine liposome hydrogel. *Dermatology*, 201, 235-241.

Ruíz-Cendoya, M., et al. (2011). Treatment of murine *Fusarium verticillioides* infection with liposomal amphotericin B plus terbinafine. *International Journal of Antimicrobial Agents*, 37, 58-61.

Sande, L., et al. (2012). Liposomal encapsulation of vancomycin improves killing of methicillin-resistant *Staphylococcus aureus* in a murine infection model. *Journal of Antimicrobial Chemotherapy*, 67, 2191-2194.

Sanders, W.E., et al. (1996). Efficacy of cefepime in the treatment of infections due to multiply resistant Enterobacter species. *Clinical Infectious Diseases*, 23, 454-461.

Schäfer, M., et al. (1996) Crystal structure of vancomycin. *Structure*, 4, 1509-1515.

Schultz, G.S., et al. (2003). Wound bed preparation: A systematic approach to wound management. *Wound Repair and Regeneration*, 11, S1-S28.

Sharma, A. and Sharma, U.S. (1997). Liposomes in drug delivery: progress and limitations. *International Journal of Pharmaceutics*, 154, 123-140.

Shaw, T.J. and Martin, P. (2009). Wound repair at a glance. *Journal of Cell Science*, 122, 3209-3213.

Stojadinovic, A., et al. (2008). Topical advances in wound care. *Gynaecologic Oncology*, 111, S70-S80.

Tang, J., et al. (2010). Pharmacokinetics and biodistribution of itraconazole in rats and mice following intravenous administration in a novel liposome formulation. *Drug Delivery*, 17, 223-230.

Torres, I.M.S. et al., (2012). Preparation, characterisation and *in vitro* antimicrobial activity of liposomal ceftazidime and cefepime against *Pseudomonas aeruginosa* strains. *Brazilian Journal of Microbiology*, 2012, 984-992.

Vancomycin. Drug Bank website [online]. 2013 [cited 28th October 2013]. Available from: http://www.drugbank.ca/drugs/DB00512.

Vyas, S.P., et al. (2007). Mannosylated liposomes for bio-film targeting. *International Journal of Pharmaceutics*, 330, 6-13.

Wallick, H. and Hendlin, D. (1974). Cefoxitin, a semisynthetic cephamycin antibiotic: Susceptibility studies. *Antimicrobial Agents and Chemotherapy*, 5, 25-32.

Watanabe, A., et al. (2010). Comparison between concentrations of amphotericin B in infected lung lesion and in uninfected lung tissue in a patient treated with liposomal amphotericin B (AmBisome). *International Journal of Infectious Diseases*, 14S, e220-e223.

Wild, T., et al. (2010). Basics in nutrition and wound healing. *Nutrition*, 26, 862-866.

Wu, P-S., et al. (2004). The characterisation and biodistribution of cefoxitin-loaded liposomes. *International Journal of Pharmaceutics*, 271, 31-39.

Yahav, D., et al. (2007). Efficacy and safety of cefepime: a systematic review and meta-analysis. *The Lancet Infectious Diseases*, 7, 338-348.

In: Advances in Liposomes Research
Editor: Lauren Finney
ISBN: 978-1-63117-074-4

Chapter 3

TRENDS ON MICROFLUIDIC LIPOSOME PRODUCTION THROUGH HYDRODYNAMIC FLOW-FOCUSING AND MICRODROPLET TECHNIQUES FOR GENE DELIVERY APPLICATIONS

Lucimara Gaziola de la Torre*, Tiago Albertini Balbino, Caroline Casagrande Sipoli, Micaela Tamara Vitor and Aline Furtado Oliveira

School of Chemical Engineering,
University of Campinas, Brazil

ABSTRACT

Recent studies on liposome production for gene delivery have aimed to obtain final formulations with physicochemical properties, like size and polydispersity in optimum ranges for biological applications without the need for post-processing steps. In this context, microfluidics emerges as a promising technology to overcome the major challenges of the pharmaceutical industry, especially for gene delivery purposes. In this field, microfluidic hydrodynamic focusing (MHF) technique and microfluidic based in droplets were used for liposomes production and to

* E-mail address: latorre@feq.unicamp.br.

complex liposomes with nucleic acids. Essentially, MHF technique is composed by a central organic stream of lipids dispersed in alcohol hydrodynamically focused by two adjacent aqueous streams; the water-alcohol diffusion along the main microchannel forms instability regions for the phospholipids that self-assemble into vesicles. Additionally, MHF technique allows the formation of monodisperse nanosized liposomes in one-step for a variety of applications. The other technique, microfluidic based in droplets, was described as an innovative and promising technique. Basically, the droplet contains the aqueous phase with liposome and nucleic acid and it is stabilized in the oil phase by a surface active compound. The main advantage of microdroplet platform is to allow more rapid mixing, generating complex with smaller size and polydispersity, forming the aggregates inside microsized droplets in emulsions. Thus, in this chapter, we summarize recent studies and trends on microfluidics liposomes context about liposomes in the microfluidic techniques context, for production of liposomes through the MHF and microfluidic droplet techniques emphasizing future applications in the gene delivery field. We hope that the main findings of the state-of-the-art disclosed herein can be useful for rational use of microfluidics devices for liposome production for formation of nonviral gene delivery systems.

INTRODUCTION

Liposomes are self-aggregate systems that have similar structure as cellular membranes and it is composed by amphyphatic lipids. Most of the lipids that are used as building blocks for liposomes are natural and it has many advantages for biomedical applications, such as low citotoxicity and biocompatibility [1]. These advantages had led the use of these aggregates in different uses, since the encapsulation of traditional drugs (doxorubicin) [2], to the use as non-viral vectors for gene delivery.

Gene delivery is a promising technique that basically allows the insertion of nucleic acid inside cells for the treatment of infectious diseases, such as tuberculosis [3-5], cancer immunotherapy [6] among others [7, 8]. The process of introducing nucleic acid inside cells is called transfection and it requires genetic material protection from different barriers (extracellular matrix, cell membrane, cytosol, nuclear membrane) [9]. In this case, since nucleic acid have anionic characteristics, non-viral vectors (with cationic characteristics) can be developed aiming at the proper genetic material condensation, protection from barriers and also direct inside cells. Among different non-viral vectors, cationic liposomes have been extensively investigated [1].

The use of liposomes as a gene delivery system requires the use of cationic lipids, which do not exist naturally and which has led to the development of different synthetic molecules [10, 11]. The cationic characteristics are important for the electrostatic interaction with nucleic acids, allowing their incorporation into liposome structures and also allowing interactions with cellular membranes that have anionic characteristics. Examples of synthetic cationic lipids are DOTAP (1,2-dioleoyl-3-trimethylammonium propane), DOTMA (2,3-bis(oleyl)oxypropyl-trimethylammonium chloride), DDAB (dimethyl dioctadecyl ammonium bromide), DC-Chol (3 β [*N-(N',N'*-dimethylaminoethane)-carbamoyl]cholesterol), DMRIE (*N*-(2-hydroxyethyl)-*N,N*-dimethyl-2,3-bis(tetradecyloxy)-1-propanaminium bromide), DOGS (dioctadecyl amino glycyl spermine), DOSPA (2,3 dioleyloxy-*N*-[2(spermine carboxaminino)ethyl]-*N,N*-dimethyl-1-propanaminium trifluoroacetate). The inclusion of phosphatidylethanolamines (DOPE) facilitates the nucleic acid to escape inside the cytosol and they are considered as helper lipids [12]. The liposome cationic characteristic offers toxicity, and it has to be very well characterized together with the development of new non-vectors for gene delivery. The inclusion of egg phosphatidylcholine (EPC) in the lipid composition demonstrated an impressive decrease in the *in vitro* cytotoxicity [3, 13].

Besides the promising results for the use of cationic liposomes as non-viral vectors for gene delivery, the development of new processes capable of producing cationic liposomes and also cationic liposomes/DNA complexes are in the early stages of development. As process requirements, the production of aggregates with physico-chemical properties (average diameter, size distribution and zeta potential) in a reproducible manner is necessary.

In this context, microfluidics emerges as a new promising technique for the production of liposomes and their complexation with nucleic acids. The understanding of this technology and how fluid dynamics influences the microscale for liposome formation allows the understanding of the actual studied processes and the development of new processes for the production of cationic liposomes and their complexes with nucleic acids for gene delivery applications.

MICROFLUIDICS – GENERAL CONCEPTS

Microfluidics is an interdisciplinary field that uses techniques that operate in devices built in micrometer scale and works with small volume of fluids. As consequence, the flow is laminar (low values of Reynolds Number) and allows integration of different techniques. Thereby, microfluidic devices need a smaller amount of reagents and have a high surface-to-volume ratio that improves heat and mass transfer, and, as consequence, these processes produce fast reactions, allowing the control and manipulation of molecules accurately in space and time. Therefore, they have the ability to mimic the cellular microenvironment and rapidly analyze biomolecules [14-16].

Microscale technology initiated with the development of microelectronics for the production of small silicon-based electronic devices. These techniques were also applied for the fabrication of mechanical devices, the microelectromechanical systems (MEMS), and after that in the medical and life sciences, known as biological microelectromechanical systems (BioMEMS). Later, this technology was adapted to create miniaturized systems as microflow sensors, micropumps and microvalves that marked the beginning of microfluidics, in the 1980s [15, 17]. The concept of microfluidics was presented by Manz and his collaborators (1990) who developed microanalytical methods, the so-called micro-total-analytical systems (μTAS) or lab-on-a-chip. This area is mainly applied to life sciences and chemical applications [14]. Following this approach, the field of microfluidics has grown rapidly with several applications [17-19].

Thus, microfluidics is a practical tool that enables advances in existing technologies in the macro scale, and it allows the possibility to obtain data in real time with the appropriate conditions, improving the performance of various assays. Different applications in microfluidics require devices that are projected with specific geometry. These devices are manufactured in different forms and materials, depending on the goal [14, 20].

Among the materials useful for biological applications, we highlight glass and some polymers. Glass has the characteristic of biocompatibility, chemistry and physical stability, and it is transparent, rigid, hydrophilic and impermeable to gases. Considering the property of glass, the manufacture of microchannels in glass can be made by laser ablation or wet etching. This latter technique consists in the use of photolithography on glass, and the channel is made by the corrosion process using hydrofluoric acid (HF) [20, 21].

Polymers can show interesting characteristics such as thermal stability, flexibility, reversible adhesion to other surfaces, biocompatibility, it is nontoxic, and the hydrophobic property allows gas exchange [22]. Among the polymers, polydimethylsiloxane (PDMS) is extensively used for the fabrication of microfluidic devices due to its intrinsic properties. However, PDMS has the characteristic of being adsorbed by hydrophobic small molecules, and its surface can affect the reaction kinetics of the cells, but there are methods for surface change [23, 24]. Other polymers that are less hydrophobic can be used to overcome these deficiencies, such as polymethyl-methacrylate (PMMA), polycarbonate and polytetrafluoroethylene, which have wide applications in analytical and biological fields [25]. Thus, there are several materials that can be applied in microfluidic system and for different research studies, as shown in Table 1.

Table 1. Main materials used for construction of microfluidic devices and applications

Materials of microfluidic device	Applications of microfluidic devices
Silicon	Chemical assays [26]; Separation process [27]; Production of liposome [28]
Glass	Cell shorting [29]; Flow cytometry [30]
SU-8	Construction 3D microchannel [31, 32]
Polydimethylsiloxan (PDMS)	Chemotaxis cell [33]; Molecules delivery [34]; Liposome/DNA complexes for DNA delivery [35, 36]
Polymethyl-methacrylate (PMMA)	Protein assay [37]; Droplet-based microfluidics [38, 39]
Polycarbonate (PC)	Capillary electrophoresis [40]; Immobilization [41] and purification of molecules [42]
Poly tetrafluoroethylene (PTFE)	Cell cultures [43]; Constructions of micro valves and pumps [44]
Hydrogels	Cell chemotaxis [45, 46]; Valves for control of autonomous flow [47]

However, the manufacturing techniques are specific for each type of material; the lithography technique is the most applied one to build microchannels for the majority them [20, 48, 49]. Furthermore, lithography is fast, cheap and suitable for most biological assays [16].

Lithography is a process that transfers image from a mask to a base by an incident light, where different types of energy beam can be used. Among lithography subcategories, one of the most applied methods is the photolithography. Another widely used method applied to construct PDMS microdevices is the soft lithography that is used for rapid prototyping (based on the photolithography method) and replica molding [48, 50, 51].

More specifically, the photolithography process consists of three steps: (i) addition of a photoresist that is spread on a base, usually a silicon wafer; (ii) superimposing of a mask (containing the geometry of the channel in the transparency) on the base; and (iii) focusing of light to demarcate the geometry. Thus, a negative mold is obtained and used for the next steps, such as the replica molding [48, 52]. Then, the cure process is carried out (using PDMS) and the device is demolded. After that , the PDMS structure is bonded to a plane substrate, for example glass (via plasma oxygen), generating the microchannel device [19, 50] (Figure 1).

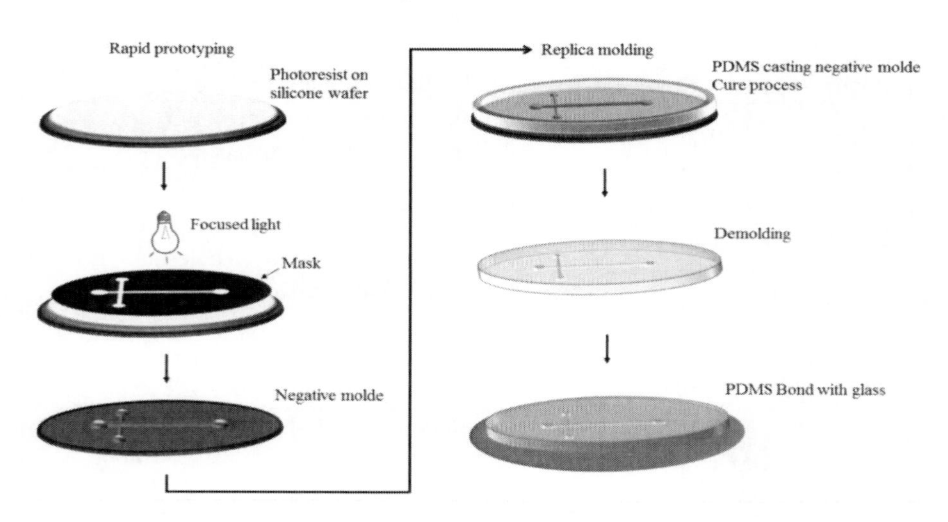

Figure 1. Steps of the soft lithography process for microchannel construction in microfluidic device.

Although the soft lithography technique is more suitable for biological applications, there are other methods that can be used for the microchannel fabrication, such as micromachining, embossing, *in situ* construction, injection molding and micromachining with laser ablation, electrochemical or ultrasonic technologies, as well as the determination of materials to be used. The proper selection of material depends on the purpose of application, and it will define the device construction technique [16, 25, 53]. Microfluidics allows applications in molecules/cell separations, such as blood cells [54]; it has the capacity to generate concentration gradients that can be applied for the investigation of the cell migration when at contact with different concentrations of chemoattractant solutions [45], and the development of new devices that allow the delivery of small molecules inside cells [34], and the design of mixers of fast analysis of biochemical reactions [55].

Microfluidics is also applied in the field of analytical chemistry, biochemistry and biological sciences and engineering areas that offer new effects and better efficiency for research studies [48]. Since this technology allows high-throughput results [56], the evaluation of chemical and biochemical reactions is possible with the possibility of real-time monitoring and the determination of bioprocess parameters [57]. Also, it can be applied for research at the single-cell level in controlled environments, analysis of protein and DNA sequencing [48].

More specifically, in the field of nanotechnology, microfluidic systems may contribute to the synthesis of nanoparticles [58-60], especially for liposome production [28, 61] allowing advances in medical applications. Liposomes have been applied in different fields, such as encapsulating of particles, cell and proteins in liposomes by microfluidic systems [62, 63]. Other important application that has been investigated is liposome production for gene delivery through microfluidic system, because the uniform size distribution of liposome has better performance in gene transfections, and transfections in emulsions (W/O) can be another way to improve the activity of transfection into cells in microfluidic devices [37]. Liposome produced by microfluidic techniques has as main advantage the control in space and time generating aggregates with homogeneity in size and distribution, and the process has high reproducibility [60]. This is an important characteristic for *in vivo* applications, whereas the size interferes in the drug delivery, transfection of genes and bio distribution that affects the therapeutic capacity [28, 64, 65].

Among different methods to produce liposome by microfluidic techniques, we can highlight:

- Hydrodynamic flow-focusing, which is a method similar to the macroscale, and which is able to high-throughput vesicle production and monodisperse with diameters from 50 to 150 nm [28, 66, 67];
- Droplet emulsion, which offers high quality on the emulsification process, that is able to form a unilamellar bilayer membrane [37, 68, 69].

These techniques are better described as follows.

HYDRODYNAMIC FLOW-FOCUSING METHOD FOR LIPOSOME FORMATION AND ITS COMPLEXATION WITH NUCLEIC ACID

Adapted from the traditional batch solvent injection, the microfluidic hydrodynamic flow-focusing (MHF) method allows the lipid-to-liposome self-assembly by controlling the convective-diffusive mixing of two miscible liquids [66]. In general, MHF devices are composed of three inlet microchannels with an outlet-mixing channel. As Figure 2 illustrates, the two adjacent aqueous (water or buffer) streams hydrodynamically focus the central stream, which contains the lipid mixture in alcohol (ethanol or isopropanol). Theoretically, the molecular diffusion in laminar flow, as influenced by convective forces, between the alcoholic and aqueous streams through the mixing channel, generates instability regions for the amphiphilic lipid molecules, which tend to self-assemble into lipid bilayer fragments (LBFs).

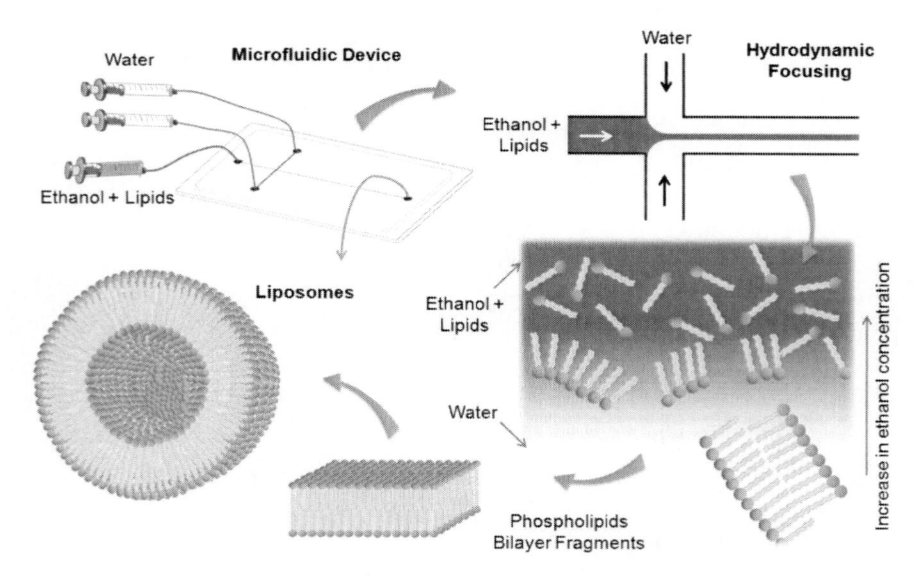

Figure 2. Schematic illustration of the hypothesized mechanism of liposomes formation using the microfluidic hydrodynamic flow-focusing method [35].

As the alcohol-water diffusion occurs and the alcohol concentration decreases, the hydrophobicity of the LBF edges promotes their self-assemble that grows until the closure into vesicles [35, 70].

Jahn et al. [66] first described the MHF method for the formation of nanoscale liposomes. In this first report, the authors produced vesicles with varying sizes by tuning the ratio of the flow rate in the adjacent and central inlet channels. To date, many research groups have studied liposome production using MHF devices with efforts to elucidate the mechanism formation of liposomes, under the particular laminar flow conditions, and also to explore their growing sort of applications.

When fluids laminarly flow inside microchannels, the region close to the microchannel walls and the interfacial region between the two species, where they are in contact to each other, might have an enhanced understanding. Experimental and theoretical studies using Y-shaped micromixers, which comprise two inlet channels and a center outlet-mixing channel, showed that, in regions close to the center of the channel, the axial distance/flow velocity ratio is related to the square root, as previously expected. Interestingly, close to the top and bottom boundaries, the width of the diffusion region is dependent of the one-third power law of the ratio between the axial distance and flow velocity [71]. These observations point to the unique behavior of the pressure-driven laminar flows in microfluidics, whose applications require a rational and particular attempt for their transport process modeling.

The advantages of using the hydrodynamic flow-focusing technique over the conventional batch systems enable the precise control of reagents mixing over the time. Previous MHF studies reported that the shortest mixing time is achieved by narrowing the width of the central focused stream [72-74]. The focusing conditions are strongly influenced by the Flow Rate Ratio (FRR), which is the ratio of the volumetric rates of the two adjacent streams to the central stream. With high focusing conditions, i.e. high FRR values, the distance for diffusion between the species is decreased and thus the mixing time is decreased. Higher focusing conditions also relies on faster depletion of the central stream after it is focused due to higher surface-to-volume ratio for the convective-diffusive mixing [70].

In general, relatively good evaluation of the complete mixing between the miscible phases can be experimentally carried out using fluorescence-based procedures or using numerical simulations [61, 72]. Meanwhile, a reasonable approximation for an order of magnitude of the mixing time is possible to be obtained. By assuming similar fluid viscosities, which implies that the average velocity of the streams are approximately the same, and based on a simple two-dimensional model, the mixing time τ_{mix} can be roughly estimated as presented in Equation 1 [58]:

$$\tau_{mix} \sim \frac{w_f^2}{4D} \approx \frac{w^2}{9\,D\left(1+\frac{1}{FRR}\right)^2} \quad (1)$$

where w_f is the width of the central stream after it is focused, D is the water-alcohol diffusion coefficient, and w is the width of the main microchannel.

Once the phospholipids are solubilized or dispersed in alcohol and spontaneously self-assemble into vesicles due to the increase in the polarity of the medium, the investigation of the mixing process between alcohol and aqueous buffer is essential for the understanding of the microfluidic formation of liposomes. Jahn et al. [61] experimentally studied the liposome synthesis using two MHF device geometries and carried out numerical modeling studies of isopropanol-water diffusion to interpret the experimental results. The results showed that the size and geometry of the microfluidic devices had little effect on liposome size distributions. This indicates that the use of larger microfluidic devices may offer technological advantages over smaller ones, mainly regarding microfabrication steps and high volumetric throughputs.

Using phospholipids with varying acyl chain lengths and consequently varying phase transition temperatures, Zook and Vreeland [70] studied in detail the effects of temperature and flow-rate ratio on MHF formation and size. The authors used a non-equilibrium kinetic model of liposome formation, in which the vesicle size is dependent of the rates of LBF growth and vesicle closure [75]. The results showed that the temperature expressively influences the liposome size, which may be more or less significant depending on the acyl chain length and the proximity of the work range of the phase transition temperatures. Most of the lipid compositions used in the work followed the trend of the lower the FRRs, the larger the liposomes are. However, the FRR behavior showed to be different depending on the formation temperature and the phospholipid used.

The MHF technique also enables an interesting way to investigate de formation of vesicles in its first stages by freezing the flow after it is focused [76]. A MHF device, which contained a rapid cooling area based on propane jet-freezing, was able to freeze the sample after the focusing. The frozen sample was collected in a receptacle with liquid propane for further analysis by means of cryo-scanning electron microscopy. The developed method allowed the observation of partially and completely formed liposomes in the aqueous-alcohol interface area between the diffusively streams.

Sonication is one of the post-processing steps for liposome size reduction and homogenization, which is generally required when liposomes are produced by conventional bulk methods. The process is based on sound energy applied by sonication that is able to rupture large multilamellar liposomes into small unilamellar ones. Huang et al. [77] produced liposomes using the MHF coupled to the sonication method, where the microfluidic device was submerged in an ultrasonic bath. The results showed that the significant reduction on liposome size and polydispersity, which is remarkably for the high flow rate ratio conditions, was likely caused by the cavitation events promoted by the sonication process.

The liposomal formulations obtained in microfluidic devices usually have low concentrations (~0.5 mM), which might have limited applications in some industrial purposes. Balbino et al. [35] produced cationic liposomes at higher concentrations than previous studies from literature using two microfluidic devices: the first one with a traditional single hydrodynamic focusing (Figure 3A), and a second one with double hydrodynamic focusing with two consecutive focusing regions (Figure 3B). The double focusing device was investigated as it is supposed to increase the diffusion surface area between the organic and the aqueous streams. The double focusing device produced cationic liposomes suitable for gene delivery at higher total volumetric flow rates when compared to the single hydrodynamic focusing. Since high lipid concentration and high volumetric throughputs imply in higher liposome productivity, the double focusing device may be a promising tool for liposome production for industrial purposes. In addition, Small Angle X-ray Scattering (SAXS) results confirmed the unilamellar nature of the liposomes produced by both devices, which was in accordance with previous morphological analysis by means of Transmission Electron Microscopy (TEM).

It is known that the conventional two-dimensional (2D) MHF is based on a sheath central stream that is formed after it is compressed by the two adjacent streams. The central flow has a columnar shape with the height of the main microchannel. Since the focused stream flows in contact with the channel walls, its parabolic velocity profile along the height of the channel varies from zero, close to the walls, to a maximum, at the channel center [78, 79]. Aiming to reduce such variation in velocity profile of the focused solution, Kennedy et al. [79] studied the liposome formation in a three-dimensional (3D) MHF device, exploring different ionic strengths of the aqueous phase. The 3D MHF devices produced liposomes in the range from 100 nm to 200 nm, using sheath-to-core ratios values ranging from ~0.5 to 23 (which would be somewhat similar to the FRR in conventional 2D MHF).

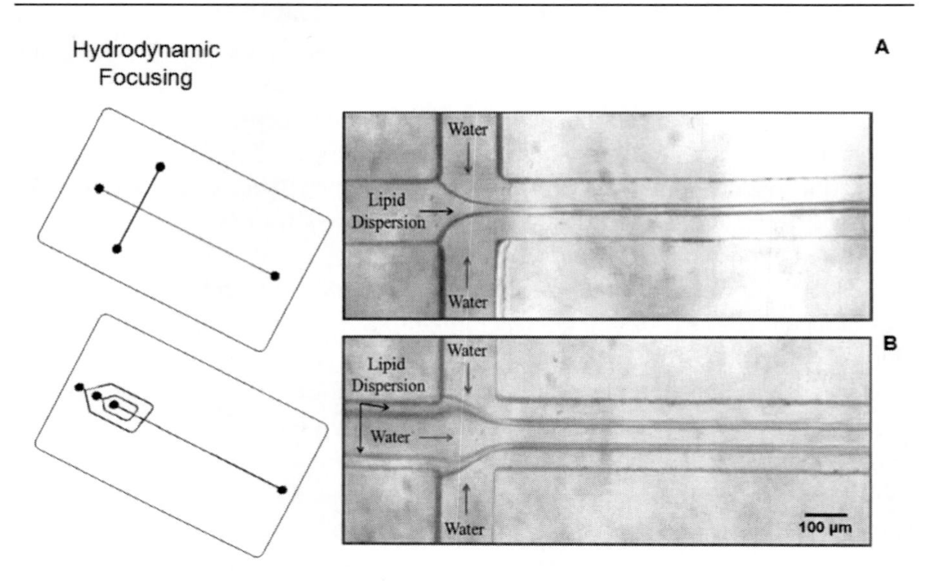

Figure 3. Microfluidic devices for production of cationic liposomes at high lipid concentrations, with single (A) and double (B) hydrodynamic focusing [35].

Microfluidic devices based on hydrodynamic flow-focusing techniques also enable the complexation between liposomes and nucleic acids in continuous flow. In general, the nucleic acid solution is injected in the central streams and is focused by the two adjacent streams containing the liposomes, as illustrated in Figure 4. In this case, all streams are in an aqueous phase, unlike the MHF for liposome formation. Otten et al. [80] first explored the flow focusing hydrodynamic technique to form complexes between multilamellar cationic liposomes and pDNA using microfluidic devices. In this study, for each position evaluated, from the focusing region moving along to the mixing microchannel outlet, the authors could observe an increase in intensity of peaks related to the intercalated layer by the pDNA and an increase in the multilamellar vesicles. Besides MHF being useful as a continuous process for the formation of pDNA/cationic liposome complexes, it also enables an excellent *in situ* characterization of lipid-based systems, which contributes to a better phenomenological understand of the pDNA/cationic liposome complexation process.

Microfluidic devices based on hydrodynamic focusing can also have different geometries to improve the mixing between species. In this case, due to compression and expansion regions, the streamlines of the fluids to be mixed have higher superficial contact area and thus the mixing occurs quickly.

In this fashion, a commercial micromixer chip with 12 successive mixing stages produced complexes of cationic liposomes and pDNA [81]. The obtained complexes produced by the MHF device presented a narrow size distribution when compared to the pipetting bulk mixing method.

Balbino et al. [36] investigated two MHF devices for the formation of plasmid DNA (pDNA)/cationic liposomes complexes. One device had the traditional flow-focusing microchannel, and another had patterned walls with uniform barriers along the main channel. For the studied molar charge ratio, in comparison to the complexes obtained in the so-called pipetting bulk mixing, the complexes obtained by the simple MHF device achieved similar *in vitro* transfection levels in human epithelial carcinoma (HeLa) cells. The pDNA/cationic liposomes complexes obtained by the patterned device yielded lower transfection levels.

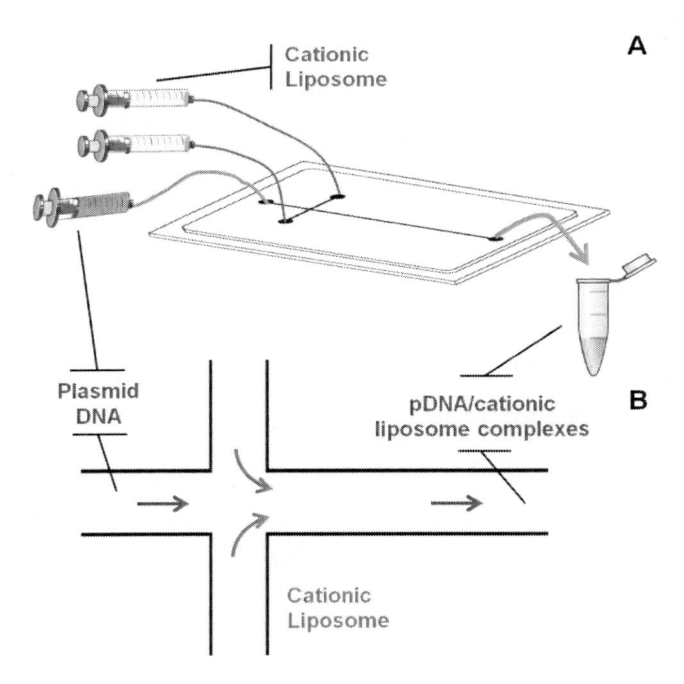

Figure 4. Schematic diagram of the microfluidic hydrodynamic flow-focusing apparatus for formation of plasmid DNA/cationic liposomes complexes (A) and the hydrodynamic focusing where the plasmid DNA stream is compressed by the two cationic liposomes streams. The formation of pDNA/cationic liposomes complexes occurs along the main outlet mixing microchannel (B).

The *in vitro* studies coupled to the physicochemical characterization indicated that these differences are most likely due to the lower pDNA accessibility of the complexes obtained in the patterned device, which may have impaired the pDNA release to the cell nucleus. These results showed that, with microfluidic techniques, the control of the transfection efficacies according to the microfluidic geometry employed to form the complexes is possible.

A microfluidic device with two consecutive flow-focusing areas was employed to produce lipopolyplexes composed of Bcl-2 antisense deoxyoligonucleotide (ODN), protamine and lipids [82]. The best configuration that was able to produce lipopolyplexes with small sizes and polydispersity comprised a pre-mixing step, in which the protamine was mixed with the lipids in alcohol and injected in the device. The complexes produced by the microfluidic device were smaller in size and presented lower polydispersity than the complexes obtained by the conventional bulk mixing process. Furthermore, the microfluidic complexes yielded better results on the down-regulation of Bcl-s protein in studies when compared to the bulk mixing complexes. This work shows the feasibility of MHD devices to produce non-viral systems with additional multifunctional properties for delivering nucleic acids [71].

Droplet Technique in Microfluidics for Liposome Formation and Its Complexation with Nucleic Acids

The generation of droplets in microfluidic compartments has been calling the attention of many researchers in the biological and chemical areas [83]. In the field of droplet technique in microfluidics, it is important to consider the concept of emulsion. Emulsion is a metastable colloid system [84] composed of two immiscible liquids, in which there is one continuous phase and a disperse immiscible phase (in the form of droplets) [85-87], which is formed after the application of shear forces and interfacial tension in the interface [86]. The presence of surfactants stabilizes the emulsion and avoid droplet coalescence, because of their groups with different affinities localized in the interface between the immiscible phases, which decreases the surface tension and ensures the long term stability of these systems [88]. Furthermore, it contributes to avoid the phenomenon called Ostwald Ripening, a spontaneous process that happens when the dispersed phase has small solubility in the continuous phase and small droplets diffuses in the direction of the larger ones and fuses them, leading to the increase of the size droplets over time and causing the emulsion coarsening [84, 88, 89]. The use of the appropriate surfactant in the emulsion process has to be extensively studied and it is not the focus of this chapter. Excellent literature can be easily found [88]. Especial attention should be taken in biochemical applications, since the surfactant has to be biocompatible for the final application [88].

Whereas microfluidics emerged as a new technology, many researchers extended basic emulsions concepts to transpose conventional methods in new microfluidic techniques in order to create different and more effective systems and processes.

The first important parameter to be evaluated in the development of microfluidic droplet processes is the selection of the appropriate materials, due to the microchannel wall wettability. In general the rule is that the continuous phase has to wet the device walls instead of the disperse phase in order to provide the droplet breakup [85, 86, 90], and in addition the wettability is decisive in the morphology of the resulting emulsion. In the case of devices produced with PDMS due to hydrophobic characteristics, only water in oil (W/O) emulsions can be prepared [85]. Chemical modifications inside the PDMS surface may change the hydrophobic nature to hydrophylic, allowing the production of O/W emulsions [91].

In general the formation of droplets in microchannels occurs through controlled pressure and volume flow rates. The immiscible liquids meet each other in junctions from the disperse phase, forming the droplets [85]. There are two different strategies in microfluidics applied in droplet generation: passive and active. In the passive methods, the droplets are generated naturally due to the channel geometries and/or liquid flow rate.

The passive methods can be divide in three different subcategories taking into account the droplet breakup geometry: (i) co-flowing stream breakup (Figure 5A), (ii) cross-flowing stream breakup (Figure 5B) and (iii) elongational or stretching dominated flow breakup (Figure 5C) [85].

Another method to produce droplets is the flow-focusing [92-94], in which two immiscible liquids flow coaxially into separate channels in a planar geometry. The continuous phase flows in both sides of the dispersed phase, and the contact of these two immiscible liquids is on the edge of the inner microchannel, and after at this point the fluids flow together.

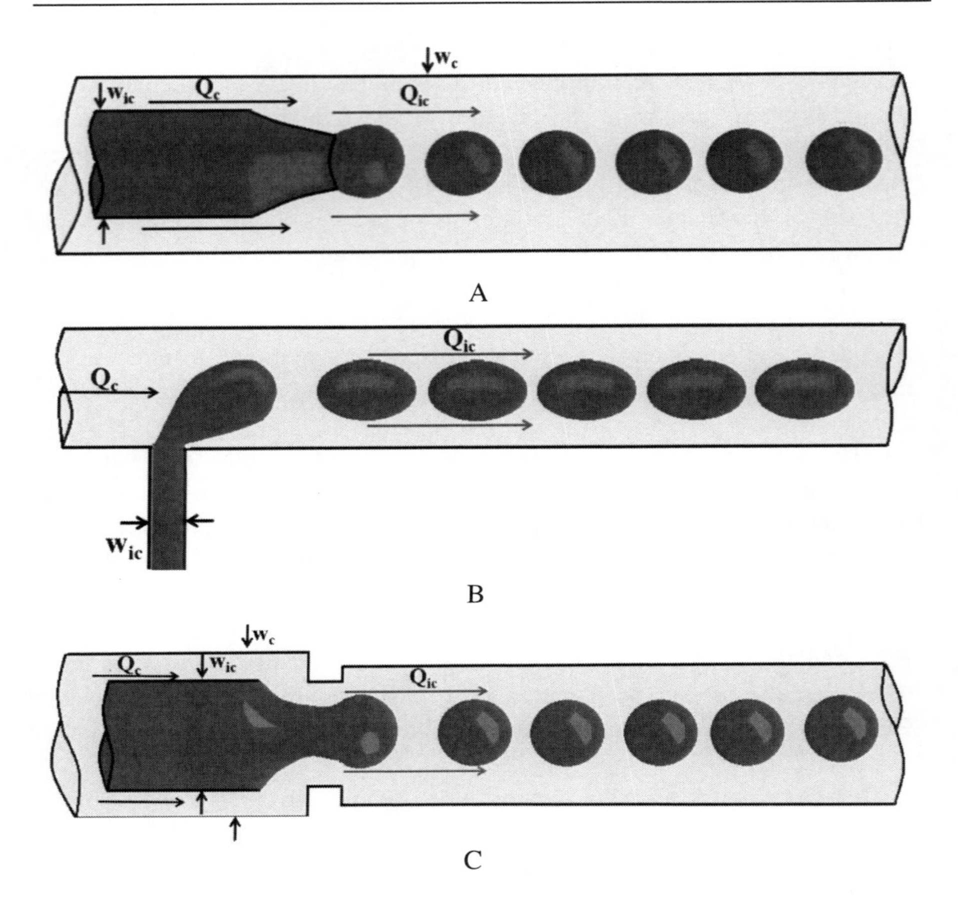

Figure 5. Droplet breakup geometries: co-flowing streams (A), cross-flowing streams (B), elongational or stretching dominated flows (C). Q_c: continuous phase flow rate, Q_{ic}: flow rate inner channels (disperse phase), w_c: channel width, w_{ic}: inner channel width.

Furthermore, the active methods use external forces to drive the formation of droplets, such as, electric field, magnetic field, optical force, heat [83, 95]. A common process in the active methods is the utilization of a piezoelectric transducer, which moves a membrane or nozzle at the end of the channel producing the droplets. Droplets are formed in jetting regime and only with the applied voltage moving the membrane [85, 96, 97].

According to Hung and Lee [95], passive methods are more simple in terms of experimental configuration, channel design and fabrication processes than active methods. They also avoid some problems caused by external forces (heating, biodegradation). However, active methods are more flexible, and a fine tuning of the flow patterns is achieved [95].

It is known that dimensionless numbers are important to establish appropriate fluid dynamic conditions to favor the generation of droplets, and Table 1 summarizes the dimensionless numbers and their definitions. The Reynolds number (Re) is the relation between the inertial forces and the viscous force and microfluidic processes that operate at Re ≤ 2 [17, 95, 98]. The capillary number (Ca) (2) is defined as the relation between the viscous forces and the surface tension between two immiscible liquids (Table 1). If Ca is small, there is the predominance of surface effects [17, 85], and as Ca increases (10^{-3} to 10^{1}) the droplets sizes are smaller [85]. The Ca can be related to volume flow rate ratio and depends on the ranges; regions that determine the droplet breakup characteristics (geometry-controlled, thread formation, dripping and jetting) can be predicted [99].

Table 2. Dimensionless numbers and definition applied to the droplet technique in microfluidics

Dimensionless Number	Equation*	Definition
Reynolds (1)	$Re = \frac{\rho UL}{\mu}$	Reynolds relates the inertial forces and the viscous force. It is applied to continuous phase.
Capillary (2)	$Ca = \frac{\mu_C U}{\gamma}$	Capillary number relates the viscous forces and the surface tension between the two immiscible liquids. It is applied to continuous phase.
Weber (3)	$We = ReCa$	Webber number relates the inertial forces to surface forces. When the viscous stress is not important if compared to the inertial and capillary forces. It is applied to the disperse phase in order to characterize the droplet breakup.
Peclet (4)	$Pe = \frac{UL}{D}$	Peclet number relates convection and diffusion.

* In the equations: ρ is density of the continuous phase, U is the average flow velocity, L is the microchannel length, μ is the dynamic viscosity, γ is the surface tension between the two immiscible compounds in the droplet system.

Anna and Mayer [99] observed that there are four droplet breakup regimes in a flow-focusing device according to the droplet formation characteristics. They systematically studied the relation among surfactant concentration, flow rate ratio (relation between the continuous flow rate and disperse flow rate) and the capillary number in order to identify the ranges for different patterns of droplet formation. These droplet regimes are named as geometry-controlled, thread formation, dripping and jetting. According to the authors, three regions existed in all surfactant concentrations (also with no surfactant); however, the thread formation is present only in a specific range of surfactant concentration. It is important to point out that when a surfactant is added to the system the capillary number in which each regime occurs increases.

The Weber number (We) (4) can also be used to characterize the droplet breakup and is applied to the disperse phase. Peclet (Pe) is applied when the process is essentially mixing (Table 2).

Multiple emulsions can be prepared in microfluidic techniques only by varying the geometry and the wettability of microchannels [94, 98]. Abate et al. [100] studied the behavior of double emulsions and, when We and Ca are higher than 1, there is not the drop formation; however, the drop formation occurs when these dimensionless numbers assume values smaller than 1.

Considering the aforementioned basic concepts for microfluidic droplet formation, advanced applications are being investigated in this field. The mixing of materials is being studied in droplet systems combining different mechanisms, such as chaotic advection [101, 102], device geometry [103, 104] and ultrasounds [105]. Droplet systems are also used for polymerase chain reactions (PCR) [106, 107]. Droplets can be used as microreactors, in which control of the reaction time is possible, which provides fast mixing of reactants and controls interface properties. Moreover, reaction in droplets are used for drug discovery, gene expression analysis and high-throughput assays and other applications [108].

Droplet microfluidics can also be used for nanoparticle synthesis [109-112] and also in giant liposome (or cell-sized liposome) formation. Teh et al. [111] prepared monodisperse lipid vesicles ranging from 20 to 100 μm using the flow-focusing droplet technique to generate a W/O/W double emulsion. The authors used the microfluidic system in two stages. In the first stage, they used flow-focusing with water in the middle inlet and two lateral inlets with oleic acid and 1,2-dioleoyl-sn-glycero-3-phosphocholine (DOPC), generating the first emulsion. Then, in the second the stage, the droplets were sheared, and double emulsion was formed in another flow-focusing with an aqueous mixture of ethanol/glycerol/pluronic (surfactant)/water. Ethanol was used in order to remove the oleic acid (OA) due to high OA solubility in ethanol. Glycerol was responsible for increasing media viscosity of the continuous phase and improving the shear in the system. The vesicle formation was the result of the self-assembly of phospholipids after OA extraction. Ethanol was evaporated and OA remained on the top of the flask where the vesicles were collected for further experiments. The authors showed that the size of the inner and outer droplets could be modulated by changing the flow rates in the second stage. The sizes of the inner droplets ranged from 18 μm to 110μm and the outer droplets from 74 μm to 110μm. They showed that 200 droplets could be prepared per second and the stability of the system was very high, as 75% of the droplets remained stable for more than 3 months. Liposomes were prepared in a 3D microfluidic pattern device and double emulsions were used as a W/O/W template. The water phase in the first emulsion was composed of deionized water with green dye, and the second water phase was composed of deionized water, glycerol and ethanol. Furthermore, the oil phase was a mixture of OA, asolectin from soybean and cholesterol, and a lipid-specific dye called Vybrant DiI Red was added to the organic phase in order to obtain fluorescent imaging [109]. The authors controlled the Ca and We numbers in order to produce double emulsions. Liposomes were obtained after the extraction of the OA existing in the double emulsions, and after that almost all droplets from the double emulsions were converted into liposomes. It is interesting to highlight that there is a critical number of phospholipids in the double emulsions that can rearrange into liposomes. If this number is smaller than the necessary to form the liposomes, the liposome rupture is inevitable. One option to avoid this rupture is the use of cholesterol, which keeps the membrane more flexible and less ruptures were observed [109, 113].

It is important to notice that techniques involving double emulsion templates for liposome formation still have the challenge of solvent removal, due to toxicity risks, depending on the application [114]. The use of solvents with low toxicity such as ethanol and also glycerol, as reported by Teh et al. [111], is an interesting strategy to overcome toxicity challenges.

Another method called lipid-coated ice droplet hydration was prepared by Sugiura et al. [115] and described by van Swaay and deMello [114]. Summarizing the technique, a previous emulsion (W/O) was prepared in microchannels, using hexane as organic phase, sorbitan monooleate (Span 80) and stearylamine as emulsifiers. The W/O emulsion had its temperature decreased, and, as consequence, the water droplets were frozen, enabling the separation of the ice droplets from the organic phase. The ice droplets were added in hexane containing egg yolk phosphatidylcholine (EPC), cholesterol, and stearylamine at -10°C to avoid ice melting. The oil phase was removed using evaporation process, and finally the aqueous phase is added to the system. This method generated giant vesicles ranging from 4 to 20 μm; however, instabilities during the hydration process could cause droplet ruptures, increasing the vesicles size.

Cell-sized liposomes formed in droplet-based microfluidic devices (larger than one micron [114]) have applications in several fields, such as molecular biology and biochemistry [116]. In most of cases, the cell-sized liposome applications are related to their large size, which allows incorporating molecules like natural genomic DNA (approximately 100 mm) [117] and carrying out gene expression in the aqueous core. Tresset and Takeuchi [118] proved that λ-DNA molecules could be entrapped inside the cell-sized liposomes protecting them from enzymes. In the same way, Nomura et al. [117] presented one or several bacteriophage T4 DNA within 35% of giant liposomes. Generally, the nucleic acids are loaded in liposomes to investigate gene expression, such as DNA transcription [63, 114] and to replicate genetic information encoded on RNA [119, 120], or to create protocells focusing on the origins of life in research studies [117]. On the order hand, nanosized liposomes, formed in flow-focusing systems, are commonly used to transport biomolecules intracellularly [63]. Wasungu and Hoekstra [121] showed another important application of the cell-sized liposomes that is to investigate, by microscopy, the mechanism of lipids (phosphatidylethanolamines and phosphatidylserines) in intermembrane interactions. These helper lipids play an essential role in the transfection of nucleic acids to cells using liposomes as carriers, since they destabilize endosome membranes by promoting phospholipid flip-flop, enabling the nucleic acids to be released into cells [122].

Droplet-based microfluidic devices have also the highlighted characteristic of achieving a rapid mixing of reagents within the system (micromixers) [17], which is important for investigating the kinetics of chemical and biological reactions [123]. The control mixing can be used to make an effective complexation between nucleic acids and liposomes [124], aiming to obtain gene delivery systems. Basically, the droplet-based microfluidic systems lead to this rapid mixing by employing special channel configuration in the design of devices [102, 125, 126]. Frequently, continuous flow microsystems (with only miscible streams) work with slow mixing, because fluids flow laminarly and mixing is promoted mainly by diffusion [123]. In contrast to this, microdroplet devices promote mixing by exploring chaotic advection, whereas two recirculation flows are generated within droplets due to the shear created between the droplets and channel wall [123] (Figure 6).

On the whole, there are two basic principles of micromixers: passive and active. The passive micromixers require different geometries, bifurcation and combination to induce secondary flow mixing. On the order hand, active micromixers demand an external energy to enhance the mixing, such as pneumatic or mechanical vibration [105, 127, 128]. Active mixers require more complex fabrication processes, and they are more difficult to integrate with other microfluidic components than passive mixers, which generally apply longer mixing length without external agitation [129-133]. Thus, droplet-based microfluidic devices composed of chaotic advection channels with different geometries are classified as passive micromixers [134], and when using a mixing electrical control they are classified as active micromixers [135].

Nevertheless, some parameters of the system have to be taken into account to provide an effective mixing within droplets. One of the most important parameter is Ca (Table 2), which should be low ($Ca < 0.001$) in order to form droplets in the system and to reach a mixture inside droplets [136, 137].The Ca is proportional to the average flow velocity (U) and inversely proportional to the interfacial velocity (γ/μ_c), hence when the flow velocity is much lower than interfacial velocity, Ca is reduced and the surface tension between the two involved phases control the system [137]. As a consequence of that, another parameter, the viscosity of fluids, interferes with the interfacial velocity and with the mixing within droplets [138]. Tice et al. [138] concluded that combination of viscous and non-viscous fluids promotes a more efficiently mixing inside drops than the use of only non-viscous fluids. Thus, the use of fluids with approximated viscosities decreases the interfacial velocity of the system, inducing a laminar regime that does not allow droplet formation and chaotic mixing [138]. Moreover, the channel configuration is also fundamental in a good mixing within the droplets, since, in large droplets, the extensive immiscible interface interferes in recirculation zones, generating stagnation points in the system and as consequences negatively interfering in the chaotic mixing mechanism [139, 140]. Furthermore, microsystems have to operate in a Peclet number (Table 2) between 1000 times and 100,000 times greater than Reynolds for a good mixing [136]. According to the Peclet number, it is possible to determine if the convection mixing (UL) or the diffusion mixing (D) dominates in the system [128]. And for the predominance of a convection mixing, a characteristically long length for the micromixer (L) is required, since average flow velocity (U) has to be low to maintain $Ca < 0.001$ [141].

Besides setting the parameters in the droplet microfluidic system, to achieve a chaotic mixing in passive micromixers, especial geometries, such as serpentine channels outlined in Figure 6, should be adopted [128]. Chaotic advection provides an accelerated mixing within droplet-based microfluidic devices, stretching and folding the fluid into droplets as long as they pass in these channels [134]. Droplets moving downstream and upstream in serpentine channels offer an alternating motion time periodically influenced by the walls, creating fluid vortexes [134]. In brief, the mechanism can be explained as follows: the part of droplet in contact with the outside arc of the channel prompts greater contact between the interface of the droplet and the channel wall, leading to a longer recirculation flow; on the other side, part of droplet in contact with the inner arc of the channel prompts smaller shear, leading to a smaller recirculation flow [142]. This process repeats along the channel, in such a way that recirculating flows vary alternately on each side of the drop, generating a chaos within it [142]. Passive micromixers with chaotic advection have a promising future in microfluidic field, since they allow an effective mixing on a millisecond scale without requiring moving parts in devices [136].

The chaotic mixing in droplet-based microfluidic devices have various applications such as: controlling chemical reactions [134], promoting protein crystallization [137] and improving biochemical analysis [143]. Among the applications, we can emphasize the complex formation between nucleic acids and liposomes (Figure 6) as an essential step in gene delivery process.

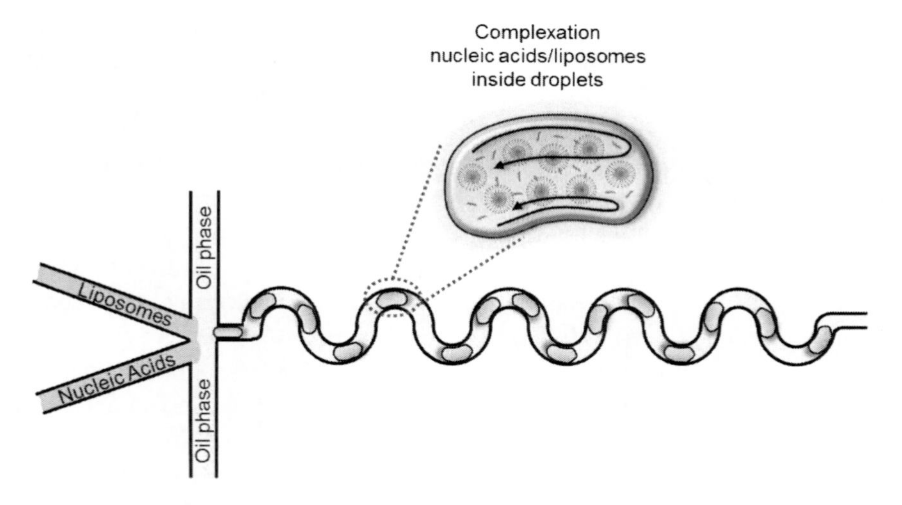

Figure 6. Scheme of liposomes complexation with nucleic acids within droplets in a droplet-based microfluidic system. Arrows represent flow within droplet.

It is well known that cationic liposomes (positively charged) spontaneously make complexes with nucleic acids (negatively charged) by electrostatic complexation, which can be formed simply by agitation, e.g. hand-shaking or vortexing [144]. However, the complex cationic liposomes/nucleic acids obtained in these processes are commonly not reproducible [145] and exhibit high size and heterogeneous population, reflecting in lipoplex uptake by cells [146-148]. Depending on the strategy used by cells to internalize lipoplexes, such as by endocytosis process [149], complexes showing small size (smaller than the endosome diameter that is about 200 nm) [150-153] and narrow size distribution (polydispersity values below 0.2) [154-156] are requested.

In this context, researchers have been exploring the use of droplet-based microfluidic systems to obtain complexes with low size and polydispersity for gene delivery applications. For example, Ho et al. [157] showed microfluidics-assisted confinement in picoliter droplets to control electrostatic self-assembly between pDNA encoding GFP and polymeric reagents, reaching complexes with approximately 300 nm in size and 0.12 of polydispersity, in contrast with approximately 400 nm in size and 0.16 of polydispersity of complexes obtained by the bulk method. *In vitro* assays with HEK293 cells showed that complexes produced in microfluidic devices presented lower cytotoxicity and higher transfection efficiency than complexes produced by the bulk method [157]. In the liposome field, Hsieh et al. [124] developed a picoliter incubator (droplets) based on the microfluidic system, which was used to constantly and uniformly mix the cationic liposomes (Lipofectin composed of DOTMA and DOPE) with pEGFP-C1 DNA vector in a serpentine mixing region. The major part of the complex population generated in the microfluidic system presented size of approximately 200 nm and polydispersity index between 0.4 and 0.45. On the other hand, hand-shaking generated a polydisperse complex exhibiting nearly three populations, one with approximately 300 nm in size, another with 700 nm and a third with 900 nm [124]. Comparing the transfection efficiencies of the two complexes through GFP expression by U2OS cells, they concluded that complexes prepared in the microfluidic system provided more consistent gene transfection (coefficient of variation of 0.05) than complexes prepared by hand-shaking (coefficient of variation of 0.30) [124].

Liposome/nucleic acid complexes obtained in the droplet microfluidic systems present characteristics also required in gene therapeutic applications. For example, when RNA is involved, they can be used against Hepatitis B and Ebola infection, hypercholesterolemia, transthyretin amyloidosis, solid cancers and lymphoma [158], in immunotherapeutic vaccine against cancer [6], to name a few; and when DNA is involved, they can be used against melanoma

[159], lung cancer [160], in the synthesis of human factor [161], among others. Therefore, the employment of a passive chaotic mixing in droplet-based microfluidic devices aiming at the nucleic acid incorporation in liposomes has a promising future.

FUTURE CHALLENGES

Although the promisor future of microfluidic hydrodynamic flow-focusing and microfluidic droplet systems in the production of nanoparticles and gene delivery applications, the scale up of processes is a very important step to enable their commercial production. One important aspect of the microfluidic systems is that scale up is related to the integration of parallel and similar microfluidic units in one device. In this case, the advantage is that the effects of mass, heat and momentum are minimized allowing the intensification of processes [56]. Schianti et al. [162] employed two microfluidic devices with four main mixing channels to carry out the rifampicin nanoprecipitation process. To distribute the aqueous and organic flows, one device had reservoirs and another had a branching system. By controlling the total volumetric rate and FRR, the authors could produce relatively monodisperse particles in the range of 250 nm. Different microfluidic production steps can also be integrated in series to satisfy all unit operations needed for a certain production. In this case, depending on the process requirements, microvalves and micropumps can also be developed to construct complex microfluidic systems, similar to electronic integrated circuits [163].

Thus, a way to overcome this drawback is to make a massive integration of devices, even though modifications in orifices and junctions can lead to a generation of different-sized droplets and varied flow rates [164]. Hashimoto et al. [165] worked in a system with multiple flow-focusing generators (two or three placed in parallel) coupled to a single outlet channel, promoting well-mixed emulsions and controlled local stoichiometry. Then this research group [166] tried another geometry by integrating two and four flow-focusing junctions in parallel, where the inlets of the continuous phase of the adjacent generators fused into a common channel and all of them emitted droplets in one wide outlet channel. In order to simultaneously obtain multiple discrete droplets with different chemical contents and concentrations, Lorenz et al. [167] developed a microfluidic droplet system in which the aqueous solution was introduced into the device, then the stream was split and merged until it reached the desirable concentrations disemboguing into the continuous oil phase to form droplets; this system is ideal to investigate the appropriate surfactant concentration to inhibit droplets coalescence. Nisisako and Torii [168] showed modules for the mass-production of monodisperse droplets, which, when operated in parallel, would be able to produce for a pilot-scale plant and, when improved with further channel integration, would be able to be used for industrial-scale production. One module was composed of cross-junctions circularly arranged forming droplets, where each of the disperse and continuous phases entered through an inlet hole flowing into a channel and then split into two streams to achieve the two droplet-formation units; differently, the other module tested was composed of co-flow junctions circularly arranged forming biphasic droplets [168]. According to Nisisako and Torii [168], these devices could be used to massively produce monomer droplets and polymeric microspheres. These works show promising alternatives to scale up process for the microfluidic production of liposomes and liposome-based complexes using the hydrodynamic flow-focusing and microdroplet techniques for applications in the gene delivery field.

FINAL REMARKS

Liposomes production based on microfluidic techniques is a promising approach that allows the investigation of different strategies, such as hydrodynamic flow focusing and droplet techniques among others. These processes offers the possibility of continuous production, however, deep understanding on flow dynamics and diffusion processes are important in order to propose new innovative processes. In terms of gene delivery applications the production of cationic liposomes and its complexation with nucleic acids is still in the earlier stages. Parameters such as shear, advection, microfluidic device geometry can influence on the final nucleic acid packing in the cationic liposomes and as consequence different transfections efficiencies can be achieved. In addition, microfluidic approach for production for these nanoaggregates and nanocomplexes will contribute for further investigation and deep knowledge on transfection processes. Furthermore, biological investigations will be better comprehended since it will be possible the production of monodisperse cationic liposomes and their complexes with nucleic acid with negligible variations on physico-chemical properties. In this instance, the effect of lipid compositions, intracellular traffic, cell uptake and transfections efficiencies, will be better explained and correlated with physico-chemical properties. Microfluidic approach for liposomes production can also offer different applications since the increase of production with reproducible physico-chemical parameters integrating parallel microfluidic units and also for new trends such as the development of personalized medicine and point of care diagnostics and treatments.

REFERENCES

[1] R. Schwendener, *Bio-Applications of Nanoparticles*, Springer, New York (2007).

[2] Y. Barenholz and A. Gabizon, *United Stated Patent* No. 4,898,735, Jun. 02,1990.

[3] R. S. Rosada, L. G. De La Torre, F. G. Frantz, A. P. Trombone, C. R. Zarate-Blades, D. M. Fonseca, P. R. Souza, I. T. Brandao, A. P. Masson, E. G. Soares, S. G. Ramos, L. H. Faccioli, C. L. Silva, M. H. Santana and A. A. Coelho-Castelo, *BMC Immunol.* 9, 38 (2008).

[4] L. G. De La Torre, R. S. Rosada, A. P. F. Trombone, F. G. Frantz, A. A. M. Coelho-Castelo, C. L. Silva and M. H. A. Santana, *Colloids Surf. B. Biointerfaces* 73, 175 (2009).

[5] R. S. Rosada, C. L. Silva, M. H. Santana, C. R. Nakaie and L. G. De La Torre, *J. Colloid Interface Sci.* 373, 102 (2012).

[6] M. T. Vitor, P. C. Bergami-Santos, J. A. Barbuto and L. G. De La Torre, *Recent Pat. Drug Deliv. Formul.* 7, 99 (2013).

[7] Y. Perrie, P. M. Frederik and G. Gregoriadis, *Vaccine* 19, 3301 (2001).

[8] S. Taetz, A. Bochot, C. Surace, S. Arpicco, J.-M. Renoir, U. F. Schaefer, V. Marsaud, S. Kerdine-Roemer, C.-M. Lehr and E. Fattal, *Oligonucleotides* 19, 103 (2009).

[9] G. Tavernier, O. Andries, J. Demeester, N. N. Sanders, S. C. De Smedt and J. Rejman, *J. Controlled Release* 150, 238 (2011).

[10] G. Byk, C. Dubertret, V. Escriou, M. Frederic, G. Jaslin, R. Rangara, B. Pitard, J. Crouzet, P. Wils and B. Schwartz, *J. Med. Chem.* 41, 224 (1998).

[11] R. I. Mahato, A. Rolland and E. Tomlinson, *Pharm. Res.* 14, 853 (1997).

[12] X. Zhou and L. Huang, *Biochimica et Biophysica Acta (BBA) - Biomembranes* 1189, 195 (1994).

[13] T. A. Balbino, A. A. M. Gasperini, C. L. P. Oliveira, A. R. Azzoni, L. P. Cavalcanti and L. G. De La Torre, *Langmuir* 28, 11535 (2012).

[14] G. M. Whitesides, *Nature* 442, 368 (2006).

[15] K. A. Addae-Mensah, Z. Wang, H. Parsa, S. Chin, T. Laksanasopin and S. K. Sia, *Microfluidic Devices in Nanotechnology: Fundamental Concepts*, John Wiley & Sons, Hoboken (2010).

[16] D. J. Beebe, G. A. Mensing and G. M. Walker, *Annu. Rev. Biomed. Eng.* 4, 261 (2002).

[17] N.-T. Nguyen and S. T. Wereley, *Fundamentals and applications of microfluidics*, Artech House, Boston (2002).

[18] G. J. Sommer, D. S. Chang, A. Jain, S. M. Langelier, J. Park, M. Rhee, F. Wang, R. I. Zeitoun and M. A. Burns, *Microfluidics for biological applications.*, Springer Science, New York (2008).

[19] D. S. C. Greg J. Sommer, Akshat Jain, Sean M. Langelier, Jihyang Park, Minsoung Rhee, Fang Wang, Ramsey I. Zeitoun, and Mark A. Burns *Microfluidics for biological applications.*, Springer Science, New York (2008).

[20] K. Sato and T. Kitamori, *Nano/Micro Biotechnology*, Springer, Heidelberg (2010).

[21] P. N. Nge, C. I. Rogers and A. T. Woolley, *Chem. Rev.* 113, 2550 (2013).

[22] J. C. McDonald and G. M. Whitesides, *Acc. Chem. Res.* 35, 491 (2002).

[23] S. H. Au, S. C. Shih and A. R. Wheeler, *BioMi* 13, 41 (2011).

[24] D. Bodas and C. Khan-Malek, *MiEng* 83, 1277 (2006).

[25] D. Qin, Y. Xia, J. A. Rogers, R. J. Jackman, X.-M. Zhao and G. M. Whitesides, *Microsystem technology in chemistry and life science*, Springer, Heidelberg (1998).

[26] E. Mery, F. Ricoul, N. Sarrut, O. Constantin, G. Delapierre, J. Garin and F. Vinet, *Sensors Actuators B: Chem.* 134, 438 (2008).

[27] N. R. Harris, M. Hill, S. Beeby, Y. Shen, N. M. White, J. J. Hawkes and W. T. Coakley, *Sensors Actuators B: Chem.* 95, 425 (2003).

[28] A. Jahn, W. N. Vreeland, D. L. DeVoe, L. E. Locascio and M. Gaitan, *Langmuir* 23, 6289 (2007).

[29] B.-Y. Qu, Z.-Y. Wu, F. Fang, Z.-M. Bai, D.-Z. Yang and S.-K. Xu, *Anal. Bioanal. Chem.* 392, 1317 (2008).

[30] M. A. McClain, C. T. Culbertson, S. C. Jacobson and J. M. Ramsey, *Anal. Chem.* 73, 5334 (2001).

[31] H. Sato, H. Matsumura, S. Keino and S. Shoji, *JMiMi* 16, 2318 (2006).

[32] R. Yang, D. L. Feeback and W. Wang, *Sensors and Actuators A: Physical* 118, 259 (2005).
[33] G. M. Walker, J. Sai, A. Richmond, M. Stremler, C. Y. Chung and J. P. Wikswo, *LChip* 5, 611 (2005).
[34] F. Wang, H. Wang, J. Wang, H. Y. Wang, P. L. Rummel, S. V. Garimella and C. Lu, *Biotechnol. Bioeng.* 100, 150 (2008).
[35] T. A. Balbino, N. T. Aoki, A. A. M. Gasperini, C. L. P. Oliveira, A. R. Azzoni, L. P. Cavalcanti and L. G. de la Torre, *Chem. Eng. J.* 226, 423 (2013).
[36] T. A. Balbino, A. R. Azzoni and L. G. de la Torre, *Colloids Surf. B. Biointerfaces* 111, 203 (2013).
[37] N. Wu, Y. Zhu, S. Brown, J. Oakeshott, T. Peat, R. Surjadi, C. Easton, P. Leech and B. Sexton, *LChip* 9, 3391 (2009).
[38] N.-T. Nguyen, S. Lassemono and F. A. Chollet, *Sensors Actuators B: Chem.* 117, 431 (2006).
[39] J. H. Xu, S. W. Li, J. Tan, Y. J. Wang and G. S. Luo, *Langmuir* 22, 7943 (2006).
[40] M.-Y. Ye, X.-F. Yin and Z.-L. Fang, *Anal. Bioanal. Chem.* 381, 820 (2005).
[41] K. G. Olsen, D. J. Ross and M. J. Tarlov, *Anal. Chem.* 74, 1436 (2002).
[42] M. A. Witek, M. L. Hupert, D. S.-W. Park, K. Fears, M. C. Murphy and S. A. Soper, *Anal. Chem.* 80, 3483 (2008).
[43] K. Ren, W. Dai, J. Zhou, J. Su and H. Wu, *Proceedings of the National Academy of Sciences* 108, 8162 (2011).
[44] W. H. Grover, M. G. von Muhlen and S. R. Manalis, *LChip* 8, 913 (2008).
[45] W. Saadi, S. W. Rhee, F. Lin, B. Vahidi, B. G. Chung and N. L. Jeon, *BioMi* 9, 627 (2007).
[46] S.-Y. Cheng, S. Heilman, M. Wasserman, S. Archer, M. L. Shuler and M. Wu, *LChip* 7, 763 (2007).
[47] D. J. Beebe, J. S. Moore, J. M. Bauer, Q. Yu, R. H. Liu, C. Devadoss and B.-H. Jo, *Nature* 404, 588 (2000).
[48] K. A. Addae-Mensah, Z. Wang, H. Parsa, S. Chin, T. Laksanasopin and S. K. Sia, *Microfluidic Devices in Nanotechnology: Fundamental Concepts*, 1 (2010).
[49] S. Colin, *Microfluidics*, Wiley, Hodoken (2010).

[50] J. R. Anderson, D. T. Chiu, H. Wu, O. J. Schueller and G. M. Whitesides, *Electrophoresis* 21, 27 (2000).
[51] Y. Xia and G. M. Whitesides, *AnRMS* 28, 153 (1998).
[52] D. C. Duffy, J. C. McDonald, O. J. Schueller and G. M. Whitesides, *Analytical chemistry* 70, 4974 (1998).
[53] H. Becker and C. Gärtner, *Electrophoresis* 21, 12 (2000).
[54] X. Chen, D. Cui, C. Liu, H. Li and J. Chen, *Anal. Chim. Acta* 584, 237 (2007).
[55] Y. Li, D. Zhang, X. Feng, Y. Xu and B.-F. Liu, *Talanta* 88, 175 (2012).
[56] T. Chován and A. Guttman, *Trends Biotechnol.* 20, 116 (2002).
[57] F. K. Balagaddé, L. You, C. L. Hansen, F. H. Arnold and S. R. Quake, *Sci.* 309, 137 (2005).
[58] R. Karnik, F. Gu, P. Basto, C. Cannizzaro, L. Dean, W. Kyei-Manu, R. Langer and O. C. Farokhzad, *Nano Lett.* 8, 2906 (2008).
[59] F. S. Majedi, M. M. Hasani-Sadrabadi, S. H. Emami, M. A. Shokrgozar, J. J. VanDersarl, E. Dashtimoghadam, A. Bertsch and P. Renaud, *LChip* 13, 204 (2013).
[60] K. Funakoshi, H. Suzuki and S. Takeuchi, *Anal. Chem.* 78, 8169 (2006).
[61] A. Jahn, S. M. Stavis, J. S. Hong, W. N. Vreeland, D. L. DeVoe and M. Gaitan, *ACS nano* 4, 2077 (2010).
[62] J. C. Stachowiak, D. L. Richmond, T. H. Li, A. P. Liu, S. H. Parekh and D. A. Fletcher, *Proceedings of the National Academy of Sciences* 105, 4697 (2008).
[63] Y.-C. Tan, K. Hettiarachchi, M. Siu, Y.-R. Pan and A. P. Lee, *J. Am. Chem. Soc.* 128, 5656 (2006).
[64] K. A. Edwards and A. J. Baeumner, *Talanta* 68, 1432 (2006).
[65] D. A. Balazs and W. Godbey, *Journal of drug delivery* 2011, 1 (2010).
[66] A. Jahn, W. N. Vreeland, M. Gaitan and L. E. Locascio, *J. Am. Chem. Soc.* 126, 2674 (2004).
[67] J. Thiele, D. Steinhauser, T. Pfohl and S. Förster, *Langmuir* 26, 6860 (2010).
[68] A. Yamada, T. Yamanaka, T. Hamada, M. Hase, K. Yoshikawa and D. Baigl, *Langmuir* 22, 9824 (2006).
[69] S. Pautot, B. J. Frisken and D. Weitz, *Proceedings of the National Academy of Sciences* 100, 10718 (2003).
[70] J. M. Zook and W. N. Vreeland, *Soft Matter* 6, 1352 (2010).

[71] R. F. Ismagilov, A. D. Stroock, P. J. Kenis, G. Whitesides and H. A. Stone, *ApPhL* 76, 2376 (2000).
[72] D. E. Hertzog, X. Michalet, M. Jäger, X. Kong, J. G. Santiago, S. Weiss and O. Bakajin, *Anal. Chem.* 76, 7169 (2004).
[73] J. B. Knight, A. Vishwanath, J. P. Brody and R. H. Austin, *PhRvL* 80, 3863 (1998).
[74] H. Y. Park, X. Qiu, E. Rhoades, J. Korlach, L. W. Kwok, W. R. Zipfel, W. W. Webb and L. Pollack, *Anal. Chem.* 78, 4465 (2006).
[75] J. Leng, S. U. Egelhaaf and M. E. Cates, *Biophys. J.* 85, 1624 (2003).
[76] A. Jahn, F. Lucas, R. A. Wepf and P. S. Dittrich, *Langmuir* 29, 1717 (2013).
[77] X. Huang, R. Caddell, B. Yu, S. Xu, B. Theobald, L. J. Lee and R. J. Lee, *Anticancer Res.* 30, 463 (2010).
[78] Y. Gambin, C. Simonnet, V. VanDelinder, A. Deniz and A. Groisman, *LChip* 10, 598 (2010).
[79] M. J. Kennedy, H. D. Ladouceur, T. Moeller, D. Kirui and C. A. Batt, *Biomicrofluidics* 6, 044119 (2012).
[80] A. Otten, S. Koster, B. Struth, A. Snigirev and T. Pfohl, *Journal of synchrotron radiation* 12, 745 (2005).
[81] R. K. Jellema, P. Bomans, N. Deckers, L. Ungethum, C. P. Reutelingsperger, L. Hofstra and P. M. Frederik, *J. Liposome Res.* 20, 258 (2010).
[82] C. G. Koh, X. Zhang, S. Liu, S. Golan, B. Yu, X. Yang, J. Guan, Y. Jin, Y. Talmon, N. Muthusamy, K. K. Chan, J. C. Byrd, R. J. Lee, G. Marcucci and L. J. Lee, *J. Controlled Release* 141, 62 (2010).
[83] Y. C. Tan, J. S. Fisher, A. I. Lee, V. Cristini and A. P. Lee, *LChip* 4, 292 (2004).
[84] J. Bibette, F. L. Calderon and P. Poulin, *Rep. Prog. Phys.* 62, 969 (1999).
[85] G. F. Christopher and S. L. Anna, *Journal of Physics D-Applied Physics* 40, R319 (2007).
[86] X. C. I. Solvas and A. deMello, *ChCom* 47, 1936 (2011).
[87] P. B. Umbanhowar, V. Prasad and D. A. Weitz, *Langmuir* 16, 347 (2000).
[88] J. C. Baret, *LChip* 12, 422 (2012).
[89] P. Taylor, *Adv. Colloid Interface Sci.* 75, 107 (1998).

[90] R. Seemann, M. Brinkmann, T. Pfohl and S. Herminghaus, *Rep. Prog. Phys.* 75, 41 (2012).
[91] W.-A. C. Bauer, M. Fischlechner, C. Abell and W. T. S. Huck, *LChip* 10, 1814 (2010).
[92] S. L. Anna, N. Bontoux and H. A. Stone, *ApPhL* 82, 364 (2003).
[93] A. M. Ganan-Calvo, *PhRvE* 69, 3 (2004).
[94] A. S. Utada, E. Lorenceau, D. R. Link, P. D. Kaplan, H. A. Stone and D. A. Weitz, *Sci.* 308, 537 (2005).
[95] L.-H. Hung and A. P. Lee, *Journal of Medical and Biological Engineering* 27, 1 (2007).
[96] B. Beulen, J. de Jong, H. Reinten, M. van den Berg, H. Wijshoff and R. van Dongen, *ExFl* 42, 217 (2007).
[97] J. Shemesh, A. Bransky, M. Khoury and S. Levenberg, *BioMi* 12, 907 (2010).
[98] S. Okushima, T. Nisisako, T. Torii and T. Higuchi, *Langmuir* 20, 9905 (2004).
[99] S. L. Anna and H. C. Mayer, *PhFl* 18, 121512 (2006).
[100] A. R. Abate, J. Thiele and D. A. Weitz, *LChip* 11, 253 (2011).
[101] H. Song, M. R. Bringer, J. D. Tice, C. J. Gerdts and R. F. Ismagilov, *ApPhL* 83, 4664 (2003).
[102] H. Song, D. L. Chen and R. F. Ismagilov, *Angew. Chem. Int. Ed.* 45, 7336 (2006).
[103] A. Goullet, I. Glasgow and N. Aubry, *MeReC* 33, 739 (2006).
[104] Y. K. Suh and S. Kang, *Micromachines* 1, 82 (2010).
[105] V. Hessel, H. Löwe and F. Schönfeld, *ChEnS* 60, 2479 (2005).
[106] K. D. Dorfman, M. Chabert, J. H. Codarbox, G. Rousseau, P. de Cremoux and J. L. Viovy, *Anal. Chem.* 77, 3700 (2005).
[107] Y. Schaerli, R. C. Wootton, T. Robinson, V. Stein, C. Dunsby, M. A. A. Neil, P. M. W. French, A. J. deMello, C. Abell and F. Hollfelder, *Anal. Chem.* 81, 302 (2009).
[108] H. Song, D. L. Chen and R. F. Ismagilov, *Angewandte Chemie-International Edition* 45, 7336 (2006).
[109] R. T. Davies, D. Kim and J. Park, *JMiMi* 22, 8 (2012).
[110] S. A. Khan, A. Gunther, M. A. Schmidt and K. F. Jensen, *Langmuir* 20, 8604 (2004).
[111] S. Y. Teh, R. Khnouf, H. Fan and A. P. Lee, *Biomicrofluidics* 5, 12 (2011).

[112] C. H. Yang, K. S. Huang, P. W. Lin and Y. C. Lin, *Sens. Actuator B-Chem.* 124, 510 (2007).
[113] J. N. Israelachvili, D. J. Mitchell and B. W. Ninham, *Journal of the Chemical Society-Faraday Transactions II* 72, 1525 (1976).
[114] D. van Swaay and A. deMello, *LChip* 13, 752 (2013).
[115] S. Sugiura, T. Kuroiwa, T. Kagota, M. Nakajima, S. Sato, S. Mukataka, P. Walde and S. Ichikawa, *Langmuir* 24, 4581 (2008).
[116] K. Tsumoto, S.-i. M. Nomura, Y. Nakatani and K. Yoshikawa, *Langmuir* 17, 7225 (2001).
[117] S.-i. M. Nomura, Y. Yoshikawa, K. Yoshikawa, O. Dannenmuller, S. Chasserot-Golaz, G. Ourisson and Y. Nakatani, *ChemBioChem* 2, 457 (2001).
[118] G. Tresset and S. Takeuchi, *BioMi* 6, 213 (2004).
[119] A. Fischer, A. Franco and T. Oberholzer, *ChemBioChem* 3, 409 (2002).
[120] H. Kita, T. Matsuura, T. Sunami, K. Hosoda, N. Ichihashi, K. Tsukada, I. Urabe and T. Yomo, *ChemBioChem* 9, 2403 (2008).
[121] L. Wasungu and D. Hoekstra, *J. Controlled Release* 116, 255 (2006).
[122] Y. Xu and F. C. Szoka, *Biochemistry (Mosc).* 35, 5616 (1996).
[123] S. Zeng, X. Liu, H. Xie and B. Lin, *Microfluidics: Technologies and Applications*, Springer, Heidelberg (2011).
[124] A. T.-H. Hsieh, N. Hori, R. Massoudi, P. J.-H. Pan, H. Sasaki, Y. A. Lin and A. P. Lee, *LChip* 9, 2638 (2009).
[125] M. R. Bringer, C. J. Gerdts, H. Song, J. D. Tice and R. F. Ismagilov, *Philos. Trans. Ser. A Math. Phys. Eng. Sci.* 362, 1087 (2004).
[126] J. D. Tice, H. Song, A. D. Lyon and R. F. Ismagilov, *Langmuir* 19, 9127 (2003).
[127] E. A. Mansur, M. Ye, Y. Wang and Y. Dai, *Chin. J. Chem. Eng.* 16, 503 (2008).
[128] P. Tabeling and Y. Lee, *Micro/Nano Technology Systems for Biomedical Applications: Microfluidics, Optics, and Surface Chemistry*, Oxford University Press, Oxford (2010).
[129] G. G. Yaralioglu, I. O. Wygant, T. C. Marentis and B. T. Khuri-Yakub, *Anal. Chem.* 76, 3694 (2004).
[130] S.-J. Park, J. K. Kim, J. Park, S. Chung, C. Chung and J. K. Chang, *JMiMi* 14, 6 (2004).
[131] M. Koch, H. Witt, A. Evans and A. Brunnschweiler, *JMiMi* 9, 156 (1999).

[132] D. S. Kim, S. H. Lee, T. H. Kwon and C. H. Ahn, *LChip* 5, 739 (2005).
[133] P. B. Howell Jr, D. R. Mott, S. Fertig, C. R. Kaplan, J. P. Golden, E. S. Oran and F. S. Ligler, *LChip* 5, 524 (2005).
[134] H. Song, J. D. Tice and R. F. Ismagilov, *Angew. Chem. Int. Ed.* 42, 768 (2003).
[135] P. Paik, V. K. Pamula and R. B. Fair, *LChip* 3, 253 (2003).
[136] N.-T. Nguyen, *Micromixers*, William Andrew Publishing, Oxford (2012).
[137] B. Zheng, J. D. Tice and R. F. Ismagilov, *Anal. Chem.* 76, 4977 (2004).
[138] J. D. Tice, A. D. Lyon and R. F. Ismagilov, *Anal. Chim. Acta* 507, 73 (2004).
[139] C. N. Baroud, F. Gallaire and R. Dangla, *LChip* 10, 2032 (2010).
[140] A. de Lozar, A. Hazel and A. Juel, *PhRvL* 99, 234501 (2007).
[141] A. D. Stroock, S. K. Dertinger, A. Ajdari, I. Mezić, H. A. Stone and G. M. Whitesides, *Sci.* 295, 647 (2002).
[142] S.-Y. Teh, R. Lin, L.-H. Hung and A. P. Lee, *LChip* 8, 198 (2008).
[143] E. Brouzes, M. Medkova, N. Savenelli, D. Marran, M. Twardowski, J. B. Hutchison, J. M. Rothberg, D. R. Link, N. Perrimon and M. L. Samuels, *Proceedings of the National Academy of Sciences* 106, 14195 (2009).
[144] P. L. Felgner, T. R. Gadek, M. Holm, R. Roman, H. W. Chan, M. Wenz, J. P. Northrop, G. M. Ringold and M. Danielsen, *Proc. Natl. Acad. Sci. USA* 84, 7413 (1987).
[145] B. H. Welter and T. M. Price, *Clin. Endocrinol. Metab.* 83, 2421 (1999).
[146] J. M. Barichello, S. Kizuki, T. Tagami, T. Asai, T. Ishida, H. Kikuchi, N. Oku and H. Kiwada, *Int. J. Pharm.* 410, 153 (2011).
[147] J. M. Barichello, S. Kizuki, T. Tagami, L. A. L. Soares, T. Ishida, H. Kikuchi and H. Kiwada, *Int. J. Pharm.* 430, 359 (2012).
[148] M. C. Pedroso de Lima, S. Simões, P. Pires, H. Faneca and N. Düzgüneş, *Adv. Drug Del. Rev.* 47, 277 (2001).
[149] A. Colosimo, A. Serafino, F. Sangiuolo, S. Di Sario, E. Bruscia, P. Amicucci, G. Novelli, B. Dallapiccola and G. Mossa, *Biochimica et Biophysica Acta (BBA)-Biomembranes* 1419, 186 (1999).
[150] T. M. Allen, G. A. Austin, A. Chonn, L. Lin and K. C. Lee, *Biochim. Biophys. Acta* 1061, 56 (1991).

[151] D. Papahadjopoulos, T. M. Allen, A. Gabizon, E. Mayhew, K. Matthay, S. K. Huang, K. D. Lee, M. C. Woodle, D. D. Lasic, C. Redemann and et al., *Proc. Natl. Acad. Sci. USA* 88, 11460 (1991).

[152] M. T. Peters, K. L. Brigham, G. A. King, B. O. Meyrick, X. Gao and A. A. Stecenko, *Exp. Lung Res.* 25, 183 (1999).

[153] J. Rejman, V. Oberle, I. S. Zuhorn and D. Hoekstra, *Biochem. J.* 377, 159 (2004).

[154] J. Kristl, K. Teskac, C. Caddeo, Z. Abramovic and M. Sentjurc, *Eur. J. Pharm. Biopharm.* 73, 253 (2009).

[155] M. Licciardi, D. Paolino, C. Celia, G. Giammona, G. Cavallaro and M. Fresta, *Biomaterials* 31, 7340 (2010).

[156] M. S. Muthu, S. A. Kulkarni, A. Raju and S. S. Feng, *Biomaterials* 33, 3494 (2012).

[157] Y.-P. Ho, C. L. Grigsby, F. Zhao and K. W. Leong, *Nano Lett.* 11, 2178 (2011).

[158] D. Haussecker, *Molecular therapy Nucleic acids* 1, e8 (2012).

[159] S. E. Parker, S. Khatibi, M. Margalith, D. Anderson, M. Yankauckas, S. H. Gromkowski, T. Latimer, D. Lew, M. Marquet and M. Manthorpe, *Cancer Gene Ther.* 3, 175 (1996).

[160] Y. Zou, G. Zong, Y.-H. Ling and R. Perez-Soler, *Cancer Gene Ther.* 7, 683 (2000).

[161] M. Baru, J. H. Axelrod and I. Nur, *Gene* 161, 143 (1995).

[162] J. N. Schianti, N. N. Cerize, A. M. de Oliveira, S. Derenzo and M. R. Góngora-Rubio, *Progress in Nanotechnology and Nanomaterials* 2, 101 (2013).

[163] T. Thorsen, S. J. Maerkl and S. R. Quake, *Sci.* 298, 580 (2002).

[164] E. Kumacheva and P. Garstecki, *Microfluidic Reactors for Polymer Particles*, John Wiley & Sons, UK (2011).

[165] M. Hashimoto, P. Garstecki and G. M. Whitesides, *Small* 3, 1792 (2007).

[166] M. Hashimoto, S. S. Shevkoplyas, B. Zasońska, T. Szymborski, P. Garstecki and G. M. Whitesides, *Small* 4, 1795 (2008).

[167] R. M. Lorenz, G. S. Fiorini, G. D. Jeffries, D. S. Lim, M. He and D. T. Chiu, *Anal. Chim. Acta* 630, 124 (2008).

[168] T. Nisisako and T. Torii, *LChip* 8, 287 (2008).

In: Advances in Liposomes Research
Editor: Lauren Finney
ISBN: 978-1-63117-074-4

Chapter 4

LIPOSOMES: IMPORTANT DRUG CARRIERS IN CANCER THERAPY

C. Vizentini-Silva, D.M. Ferreira and A.C. Tedesco
Departamento de Química, Laboratório de Fotobiologia e Fotomedicina, Centro de Nanotecnologia e Engenharia Tecidual, Faculdade de Filosofia, Ciências e Letras de Ribeirão Preto, Universidade de São Paulo, Ribeirão Preto-SP, Brazil

ABSTRACT

Normal human cells grow, multiply and die, by it self control process. When there is loss of this cell control it start a fast and reproducible division that may lead to the invasion to other normal cells and tissues. This uncontrolled growth and aggressive process, in most of the cases, featuring a set of more than 100 different types of diseases called normally as cancer. Among the forms of treatment for cancer in general, chemotherapy, radiotherapy and surgery are the most acceptable and used, (alone or combined), however, early diagnosis is essential for effective healing or eradication of the diseases. These treatments do not affect only the damaged tissue and cause undesirable side effects such as hair loss, nausea and other, increased risk of infections, asthenia, intestinal obstruction and even mutilation once in some cases surgery compromise patient life, may lead to irreversible psychological damage. Therefore there is a need for new therapeutic methods that enable reduction of the tumor and restricting adverse effects to diseased tissue while protecting the healthy tissue. These could be archive by the use of specific drugs in the conventional treatments as well as with new therapeutic approaches whose goal is to reducing the tumor size and spread process and with protocol minimally invasive with restriction of adverse effects in the diseased tissue what is essential for achieving a successful outcome. Liposomes as Drug delivery system have been studied over the last 3 decades as DDS with special appeal when applied to anti-cancer therapy and to treat many other diseases. Standing out among the nanosized systems for drug delivery because they allow the incorporation of hydrophobic drugs in the lipid bilayer and hydrophilic drugs in the aqueous phase, while maintaining their physical and chemical characteristics, as well as promoting their selective distribution in tissues when incorporated efficiently to liposomes. This selective distribution in tissues is greater in the case of cancer cells, since these have high metabolism and require higher nutrient. This chapter provides a general approach with the discussion of the liposome research focusing in cancer treatment and the introduction of two new liposomal system applied in combination with a an alternative protocol know as photodynamic therapy (PDT), one of them containing cisplatin - conventional chemotherapeutic - for synergistic effect with the chloro-aluminum phthalocyanine and other containing folic acid vetorizador of the drug to treat mamarin and other visceral cancers.

Normal human cells grow, multiply, and die through a self-controlled process. When the cell loses control, it starts a fast and reproducible division and may invade normal cells and tissues. In most cases, this uncontrolled and aggressive process soon causes over 100 different types of diseases normally designated as Cancer. Among the various strategies to treat cancer, chemotherapy, radiotherapy, and surgery are the most widely accepted methods, used, alone or in combination (Ministério da Saúde, INCA, 2011) However, early diagnosis is to effectively cure cancerous diseases. Unfortunately, the currently available treatments do not affect the damaged tissue only, indeed, they cause undesirable side effects such as hair loss, and nausea, as well as increased risk of infections, asthenia, and intestinal obstruction. In some cases, surgery can negatively affect the patient's life: mutilation might be necessary, eliciting irreversible psychological damage (Ministério da Saúde; INCA, 2011). Therefore, it is crucial to find new therapeutic methods that can reduce tumor size in the case of great tumor mass, which in turn will decrease the margin tumor resection. Restricting the adverse effects to diseased tissues while protect the healthy tissue is also desirable. To achieve successful outcome it is necessary to combine well-designed, specific delivery of conventional drugs with new therapeutic approaches that could reduce the tumor size associated with metastasis. To this end, it is essential to adopt a minimally invasive protocol, to restrict the adverse effects to the diseased tissue (Agostinis et al., 2011; Ally et al., 2005; Bolfarini et al., 2012; Cho et al., 2008; De Paula et al., 2012).

Over the last 15 years, many strategies focusing on specific drug delivery have emerged. The most promising approach has been to develop micro and nanostructured system known as Drug Delivery Systems (DDS) which have led to excellent results. Among the existing DDS, the most remarkable are liposomes (Barbugli et al., 2010; Maranho et al., 2009), biodegradable nanospheres (Simioni et al., 2011), nanoemulsions (De Paula et al., 2012; Primo et al., 2008), nanocapsules (Oyarzun-Ampuero et al., 2013; Vergara et al., 2012), and nanospheres (Lu et al., 2006; Shen et al., 2011).

Over the last ten years, liposomes have attracted attention as classic and well-designed DDS to treat cancer and many other diseases (Chen et al., 2010; Duzgunes & Nir, 1999; Gabizon, 1995; Schmid & Korting, 1996; Woodle, 1995; Yang et al., 2011). Liposomes stand out among nanosized DDS: they incorporate hydrophobic drugs in the lipid bilayer and hydrophilic drugs in the aqueous phase, while maintaining their physical and chemical characteristics. Additionally, they selectively distribute drugs in tissues (Hoebeke, 1995), particularly in the case of cancer cells, which have high metabolism and require larger amounts of nutrients (Cairns , Harris e Mak, 2011; Nguyen , Bos e Massague, 2009).

This chapter discusses research into liposomes for use in cancer treatment, especially skin and visceral cancer. It also introduces two new liposomal systems combined with an alternative clinical protocol known as photodynamic therapy (PDT). One of these systems contains cisplatin – a conventional chemotherapeutic drug associated with chloro-aluminum phthalocyanine (ClAlPc) photoactivation process, to produce a synergistic effect. The other system also involves ClAlPc as photosensitizer combined with DDS based on liposomes modified with molecules such as folic acid (as an additive), to deliver the drug to the target tissue during the treatment of breast cancer and its derivative cells and of other visceral cancers. Finding alternative ways to treat breast cancer is mandatory, because this disease accounts for one of the highest mortality rates among cancers affecting women.

The World Health Organization (WHO) defines cancer as the uncontrolled spread of damaged cells that have lost their internal growth control and which multiply and undergo apoptosis during their life time. Unfortunately, good prognosis only exists for the disease detected in initial or little advanced stages a favorable outcome will depend on the type of affected organ or tissue.

Therefore, it is crucial to improve the therapeutic efficiency and minimize the side effects of currently available medications.

Anticancer therapy involves the systemic administration of chemotherapeutic drugs and ends up exposing all the tissues to different concentrations of cytotoxic drugs. Hence, it is necessary to establish dose administration regimes that will ensure active constant drug release at doses large enough to induce tumor cell killing, or activation of immunologic response (Morgan et al., 2010), while minimally harming non-cancerous tissues (Jackson et al., 2011). Since, the earliest development of chemotherapeutic treatment (Li and Chignell, 1987) the search for a specific way to deliver the drug to the tumor tissue has been one of the primary and most challenging goals in cancer therapy. Researchers have discovered several drugs; they have also proposed, used, and tested a number of DDS, looking for the best way to target the unhealthy tissue instead of the normal one. More recently, studies (Gao, Zhang & Sun, 2012) have been redirected to cater for the development of new micro and nanosized systems as target-specific DDS (Suzuki et al., 1996; Petrak, 2005; Harashima & Kiwada, 1996).

Today, countless types of DDS associate a photosensitizing drug with other active compounds, for use in systemic and / or topical cancer treatment (Nunes, 2004; Maranho et al., 2009; Derycke & De Witte, 2004; Molinari et al., 2007; Nombona et al., 2012). The interest in micro and nanoscale DDS has grown exponentially in the last decade (Laouini et al., 2011; Primo et al., 2007; Simioni et al., 2007), because these new developments have improved the delivery, biocompatibility, and biodistribution of the active compounds.

Liposomes make interesting DDS: added to drug formulations, they help to circumvent issues related to unfavorable physicochemical properties of drugs, facilitating drug delivery to the target tissue. Most of the molecules used in PDT treatment bear a well-conjugated framework structure that absorbs light in the final part of the visible electromagnetic spectrum – between 600 and 780 nm, orange to near red color) (Bonnett, 2000; Zenkevich et al., 1996; Ricchelli, 1995). Liposomes offer many advantages: (1) they are similar to and have affinity for biological membranes, and (2) they can compartmentalize various substances with different structures, diminishing their toxicity. It is possible to obtain liposomes from natural (Batista, Carvalho & Magalhães, 2007; Fan et al., 2013; Hayashi et al., 2011; Maherani et al., 2012) or synthetic lipid sources.

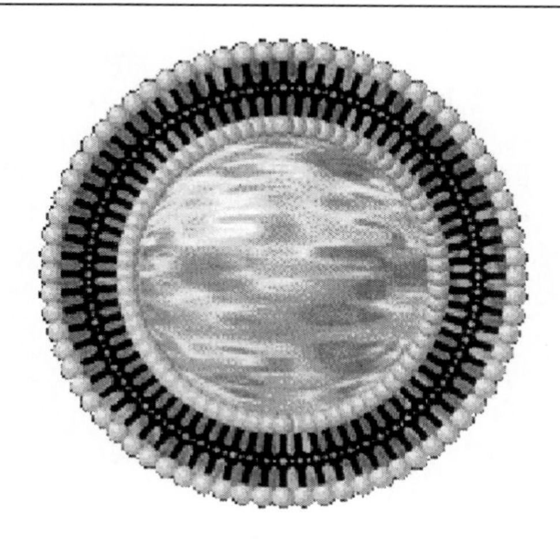

Figure 1. Schematic representation of a liposome (NUNES, S. M., 2003).

Figure 1 depicts a schematic representation of liposomes, which consist of spherical concentric phospholipidbilayer vesicles that can spontaneously arrange themselves in aqueous (Gregoriadis, 1984). This structure is common to anionic, cationic, and zwitterionic phospholipids and resembles the structure of the cell membranes. Hence, phospholipids have high affinity for cell bilayers and undergo fast uptake by classic biological processes (Fan et al., 2013; Kaye & Richardson, 1979; London, 2013). Micro and nanosized liposome-based DDS can incorporate hydrophobic drugs (in the lipid bilayer) and hydrophilic drugs (in the aqueous phase), while maintaining the physical and chemical characteristics of the drug. They also promote selective distribution of the incorporated drug in tissues (Hoebeke, 1995; Gabizon, 1995; Harashima & Kiwada, 1996; Santos & Castanho, 2002).

Several studies have associated known chemotherapeutic agents with liposomes. The literature contains examples of liposomes incorporated with doxorubicin (Gabizon, 1995), docetaxel (Liu et al., 2010) and cisplatin (Lv et al., 2013).

Cisplatin CDDP (Cis) is one of the most widely used antineoplasic agents. This drug is employed to treat gynecological, gastrointestinal and head and neck cancer. It is generally injected intravenously into the patient. However, the use of CDDP causes problems associated with intravenous administration, like: (i) systemic side effects such as nephrotoxicity, myelosuppression and nausea and (ii) delivery of low drug concentration to the biological target. (Konishi et al., 2003; Paiva et al., 2011). In this context, the use of DDS has emerged as an excellent strategy to overcome mechanisms of resistance and increase drug selectivity toward cancer cells, reducing negative side effects. (Niziolek, Korytowski & Girotti, 2003; Bisby, Mead & Morgan, 2000).

IT is possible to enhance the effect of liposomes against cancer by combining DDS with an efficient therapeutic modality, and target systems. In this field, Photodynamic Therapy (PDT) has grown significantly and has great potential (Agostinis et al., 2011; Longo et al., 2013; Paszko et al., 2010; Primo et al., 2007; Simioni et al., 2008; Siqueira-Moura et al., 2013; Triesscheijn et al., 2006). We have recently evaluated the efficiency of a liposomal formulation containing chloro-aluminum phthalocyanine (ClAlPc) as photosensitizer and folic acid as target agent, to act against breast cancer cells. Another study has demonstrated a positive interaction between Cis and PDT against esophageal carcinoma cells: indicating cell death occurred by both apoptosis and necrosis (Compagnin et. al, 2010). A liposomal formulation that combines ClAlPc with Cis in the same DDS has been shown to be a promising system to treat head and neck cancer by PDT *in vitro*.

PDT is a medical procedure approved by the FDA and other regulatory agencies since the 1990s. It constitutes that have a minimally invasive treatment and can exert selective cytotoxic activity toward cancer cells (Liu et al., 2010). PDT relies on the ability of the photosensitizer drug (PS) to selectively accumulate in tumor tissues. The PS can absorb light at a certain wavelength (typically visible) in the presence of molecular oxygen, thereby damaging or killing cells (Liang et al., 2011). PDT has three essential components: photosensitizer, light, and molecular oxygen. None of these agents is individually toxic, but together they begin a sequence of photochemical and photobiological reactions that generate singlet oxygen ($^1O_2$) and other reactive species (Agostinis et al., 2011; Dougherty et al., 1998). This characteristic is crucial to minimize side effects, because only the PDT activated by visible light will initiate the biological response, avoiding damage to healthy cells that do not receive the photoactivation by light (DE Paula et al., 2012; Primo, Bentley & Tedesco, 2008; Siqueira-Moura et al., 2013).

Photodynamic sensitizers produce reactive oxygen species. In the triplet excited state, most of the photoactive molecules can induce primary reactions with neighboring molecules through electron (or H atom) transfer, called type I mechanism, or energy transfer, known as type II mechanism. Localized singlet oxygen and superoxide (O_2^-) production elicits a cytotoxic response activated by visible light irradiation (Agostinis et al., 2011; Derosa & Crutchley, 2002; Simioni et al., 2008; Sobolev, Jans & Rosenkranz, 2000). Therefore, the essential goal of PDT is to induce cell death in tumor tissue by activation of photosensitizing necrotic or apoptotic pathways, while minimizing damage to surrounding tissues and undesirable side effects during the treatment (ZHOU, 1989).

Folic acid is an interesting additive and specific target agent in DDS: it directs the drug under study to the cancer tissue. It is useful in the therapy of various types of cancer but more specifically gynecologic. Indeed, the folate receptor is over-expressed on the surface of many cancer cells such as ovarian, endometrial, breast, lung, and kidney cancer cells (Asai, 2012; Liu et al., 2010; Peng et al., 2011; Valencia et al., 2011). In addition, folic acid is very stable, displays minimal immunogenicity, and is compatible with both organic and inorganic matter. Therefore, folic acid is potentially applicable as additive in targeted tumor therapy (Peng et al., 2011).

In another recent study, our group incorporated Cis and phthalocyanine into a different liposomal system. To this end, we prepared a cationic liposome using the thin lipid film method. (Robertson, Hawkins & Abrahamse, 2009) associated with the cationic surfactant stearylamine which provided the formulation with colloidal stability (Wongsagonsup et al., 2005). The lipid bilayer composition determines liposome stability, so selecting bilayer components appropriately will ensure the desirable fluidity or rigidity to make the most of the system's loading proprieties. For example, the addition of cholesterol to the liposome enhances lipid bilayer fluidity and makes liposomes more stable presence of biological fluids such as blood (Drummond et al., 1999). The preparation method can also influence liposome homogeneity and stability.

To prepare the liposomal formulation containing ClAlPc and folic acid, our group used the ethanol injection method described in the literature, with adaptations (Barbugli et al., 2010; Simioni et al., 2008). We injected an ethanolic solution containing 1,2-distearoyl-sn-glycero-3-phosphocholine (DSPC), cholesterol, and an appropriate volume of PS (ClAlPc in ethanol) was injected into a thermostatized jacket containing phosphate buffer, pH 7.4. Inside a cylindrical container with diameter of 2.0 cm; the solution was injected approximately 2.5 cm below the liquid surface, at 56° C under magnetic stirring, in the dark, at a rate of 360 μL h^{-1}. We prepared empty liposomes (without PS and folic acid) and liposomes containing folic acid only, for use as reference in comparative studies. We added folic acid into the aqueous phase, at concentrations ranging from 0.5 to 1.0 mmol/L. We monitored particle size the polydispersity of the liposomes in the absence and in the presence of folic acid for a period of 2 ½ months, to check how incorporation of this additive affected liposomal formulation and stability.

A cationic liposome containing both ClAlPc and Cis was prepared by the thin lipid film method (Robertson, Hawkins and Abrahamse, 2009). Briefly, egg chicken phosphatidylcholine, cholesterol, stearylamine, and ClAlPc were dissolved in of chloroform/methanol (3:1, v/v) under magnetic stirring. The solvents were removed under reduced pressure for 60 min (37 ºC, 100 rpm) until complete dryness a thin lipid film. Then, the film was hydrated with 10 mL of phosphate buffer solution (PBS 10 mM, pH 7.4) containing Cis solution, leading to spontaneous formation of multilamellar liposomes. The as-produced vesicle suspensions were extruded through polycarbonate membranes with decreasing pore sizes four times, using the high pressure extruder. The final liposomes were stored in sterile 10 mL vials at room temperature. In addition to the unloaded liposome (U) and the liposome containing both ClAlPc and Cis (LCisClAlPc), liposomes loaded with either ClAlPc (LClAlPc) or Cis (LCis) were prepared for this study.

Both U and LCisClAlPc had an average diameter below 200 nm, which is very important: macrophafes rapidly remove large liposomes from the circulation whereas they recognize an phagocyte small liposomes (liposomes nanoscale - SUV - Small Unilamellar Vesicles) more slowly, allowing the latter longer circulation time in the body and increasing the probability that the DDS will penetrate the cancer cell (Barbugli et al., 2010). The polydispersity index was less than 0.3, indicating that a homogeneous liposomal vesicle dispersion, favoring DDS stability.

Figure 2 contain a graph of the particle size measured for the empty liposome, the liposome containing only ClAlPc and the liposome containing ClAlPc and folic acid along time – for liposomes prepared by the ethanol injection method. The liposomes were stable during the entire period study, and their particle sizes were very close.

Besides these features, the cationic liposome system presented a strong positive charge with values ranging from 41.5 to 58.3 mV. The positive charge resulted from the cationic surfactant stearylamine and was important because its value offered an estimate of the colloidal stability of the formulation. The system remained stable for at least three months. Zeta potential values higher than |30| mV can stabilize suspended liposomes because vesicles undergo mutual electrostatic repulsion, which prevents them from aggregating (Wongsagonsup et. al, 2005). We investigated of the spectroscopic properties of both ClAlPc and folic acid, by directly measuring the absorption (in the 300-800 nm and 250-800 range for ClAlPc and folic acid, respectively) and fluorescence emission (wavelength of physical excitation at 615 nm and emission in the range of 650-700 nm with a maximum at 680 nm for ClAlPc).

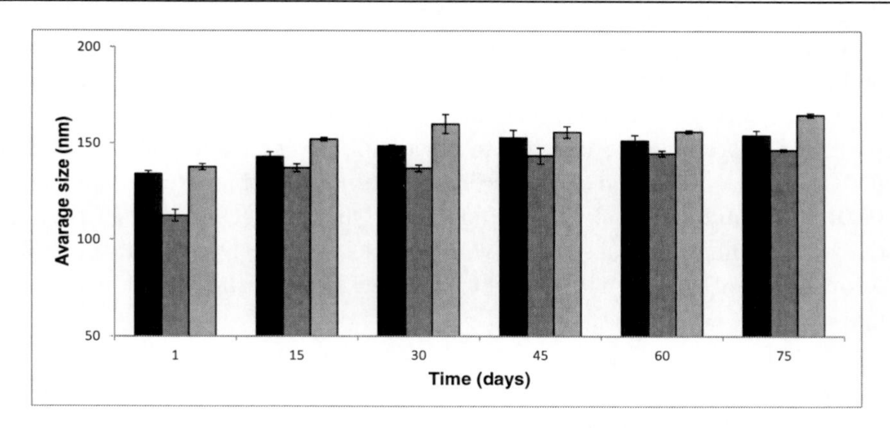

Figure 2. Average particle size of the empty liposome, the liposome containing only ClAlPc, and the liposome containing ClAlPc and folic acid along 75 days.

To analyze the properties of liposomes by spectrophotometry it was necessary to break the liposomal vesicle by adding of acetonitrile under stirring at 56 °C (lipid transition temperature) followed by centrifugation at 5000 rpm for 20 min at 4 °C, according to the work of Primo, F. L. (Primo, F. L., 2009). Figure 3 displays the set of characteristic ClAlPc absorption bands for the electronic transitions in the region of 300 - 400 nm (near ultraviolet, Soret band) and for the vibrational transitions in the region of 600 - 800 nm (red and near infrared, Q bands). The Q band is crucial to obtain efficient PS, because it lies within the so-called "therapeutic window" (600-800 nm).

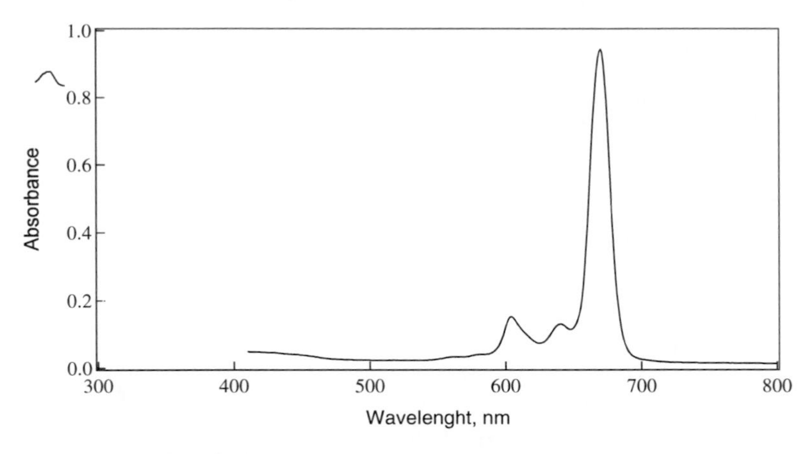

Figure 3. Absorption spectrum of ClAlPc in ethanol λ_{max} = 670 nm (Q-band).

The phthalocyanine macrocycle resonance involves four benzene rings and four pyrrolic units, leading to a strong absorption band in the red region of the visible spectrum. This is an advantage over PS drugs such as Photofrin®, a porphyrin representative that has low activation wavelength (in the range of 630 nm), and prolonged surface retention time, favoring skin toxicity after PDT and limiting its application in cancer therapy (JORI, 1996). Because ClAlPc exhibits strong absorption within the therapeutic window, it is possible to treat deeper cancers with it: light penetrates more easily into skin tissue in this range.

The fluorescence spectra of free PS and liposome-encapsulated PD after vesicles destruction have the same profile, with maximum emission at 678 nm. Thus, phthalocyanine encapsulation did not significantly shift emission bands, indicating that the PS drug did not aggregate or degrade.

After the PS drug absorbs a light photon an excited singlet electronic state becomes populated and can return to its ground state through a relaxation process or by radioactive transition, the fluorescence emission. If the PS drug reaches the excited triplet state with good quantum yields, it can generate ROS, especially singlet oxygen, the main photodynamic agent in this case.

One of the classic therapies of non-melanoma skin cancer consists of using PS drugs in PDT (Agostinis et al., 2011). Researchers have designed many types of PS agents to treat various types of cancers. The use of chemotherapeutic agents such as Cis to treat head and neck cancer is the most traditional (Bednarski, Mackay and Sadler, 2007). However, the side effects are numerous and the disease recurrence rate is high (Konishi et al., 2003). Some preclinical studies have shown the advantages of combining Cis and PDT.

Determining the cytotoxicity of the formulations is important: it helps to evaluate biocompatibility and establish a safe concentration range that will ensure achievement of the target while minimizing damage to healthy cells (Simioni et al., 2008).

To assess the biocompatibility of the cationic liposome formulations, we treated U87MG cells were treated with unloaded drugs (ClAlPc or Cis), with liposomes containing ClAlPc or Cis, and with a liposomal system containing the two drugs, all in the absence of light. After 3h of incubation, cell viability was 95% for the cells exposed to the drugs and the liposomal systems. The results demonstrated that the formulations were biocompatible in the absence of light. To assess how light affected liposomes containing both drugs, were treated U87MG cells with a predefined PDT protocol we irradiated the cells with light of 630 nm in sterile conditions at a light dose adjusted to

150 mJ.cm^{-2} and power of 90 mW. Experiments indicated that the drugs combined in the liposome system diminished cell viability as compared with the two free individual drugs. Flow cytometry using Annexin-V-Fluorescein and propidium iodide (PI) allowed us to distinguish viable cells from necrotic cells; cell labeling with a cell surface marker enable cell characterization. For example, glioma cells treated with the light dose described above and the liposomal system containing both drugs had their viability reduced to about 60%.

According to Figure 4, the phototoxic effect killed cells by either necrosis or apoptosis. ClAlPc-nduced apoptosis prevailed after PDT in accordance with some researcher's observations (Luo and Kessel, 1997). At low laser irradiation doses, damage occurred to mitochondria, lysosomes, and DNA (fragmentation). On the other hand, addition of Cis to the liposome system containing ClAlPc damaged the cell membrane: permeability to the dye PI increased, which is characteristic of cell necrosis. The duo predominant markup indicated that combining two potent drugs with PDT ensure cell death and possibly contributed to disease regression.

We used liposome containing folic acid and ClAlPc *in vitro* cytotoxicity and phototoxicity assays on MCF7 cells, a human breast cancer cell line. The liposomal formulation proved to be biocompatible, with cell viability of about 100%. Biocompatibility combined with suitable biodistribution favored the use of this system *in vivo* protocols.

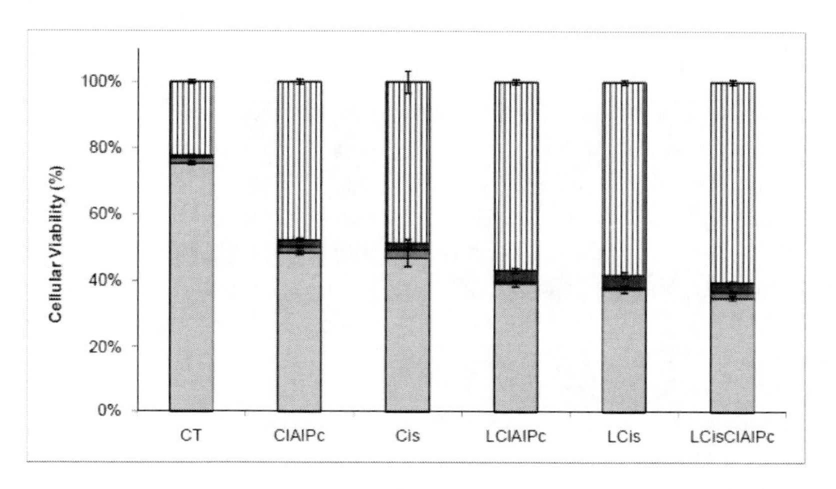

Figure 4. Graphic representation of the mean values and standard deviation of Annexin-V, PI, Annexin-V + PI positive cells percentage and unmarked cells according to the different experimental conditions.

Low cytotoxicity indicates fewer side effects after systemic, topical, or transdermal administration of the formulation (Primo, F. L., 2009). On the basis of cytotoxicity studies, we established working conditions to apply these systems in combination with PDT. The highest concentration of liposome-encapsulated PS tested here displayed no toxicity in the dark, which is essential for the conduct PDT studies (Barbugli et al., 2010). We adopted the fixed concentration of 0.5 $molL^{-1}$ ClAlPc to test liposomes containing encapsulated ClAlPc and/or folic acid under light irradiation.

In the case of free ClAlPc, cell viability was about 15% at a 670 nm light dose of 150 $mJcm^{-2}$, at 100 mW. In these same light irradiation conditions, the liposomal formulations led to significant cell death, reaching 98% cytotoxicity.

The high rate achieved for cell death metastatic cancer upon application of laser light constituted an excellent result: it proves that ClAlPc was an efficient PS drug, agreeing with results from previous studies (Siqueira-Moura et al., 2013) and being even more effective for the light dose of 150 $mJcm^{-2}$ in some cases (Barbugli et al., 2010; De Paula et al., 2013). We detected this effect after 3h of incubation, therefore, this formulation internalized satisfactorily in the tumor cells. Additionally, cell death was more pronounced in the case of ClAlPc-encapsulated, pointing to more efficient intracellular PS drug delivery, as expected.

Next, we performed cellular internalization studies, to better understand how the liposomes interacted with cells. We choose a human keratinocytes cell line, HaCat, for comparison studies with MCF7 cells – in healthy tissues epithelial cells express the folate receptor (Kelley , Rowan & Ratnam, 2003) at lower concentrations as compared with neoplastic cells, especially in the case of breast cells.

For confocal microscopy analysis, we seeded MCF7 cells (1×10^5 cells/well) and HaCat cells (2×10^5 cells/well) in 24-well plates on coverslips. After 24h, we incubated the cells (37 °C and 5% CO_2) with the formulations containing 0.5 mol/L^{-1} ClAlPc for 3h. Then, we fixed the cells with 4 % paraformaldehyde for 20 min, washed them with Hanks buffer, and marked them with DAPI, to better visualize the nucleus. We observed in the coverslips under a confocal microscope model LSM T – PMT from Zeiss equipped with a phthalocyanine filter (near 630 nm); we and photographed the samples using the equipment software.

The confocal microscopy images obtained for MCF7 cells (Figure 5) and HaCat (Figure 6) depict the intracellular distribution profile of the PS drug. ClAlPc (red) preferentially accumulated in the cell cytoplasm.

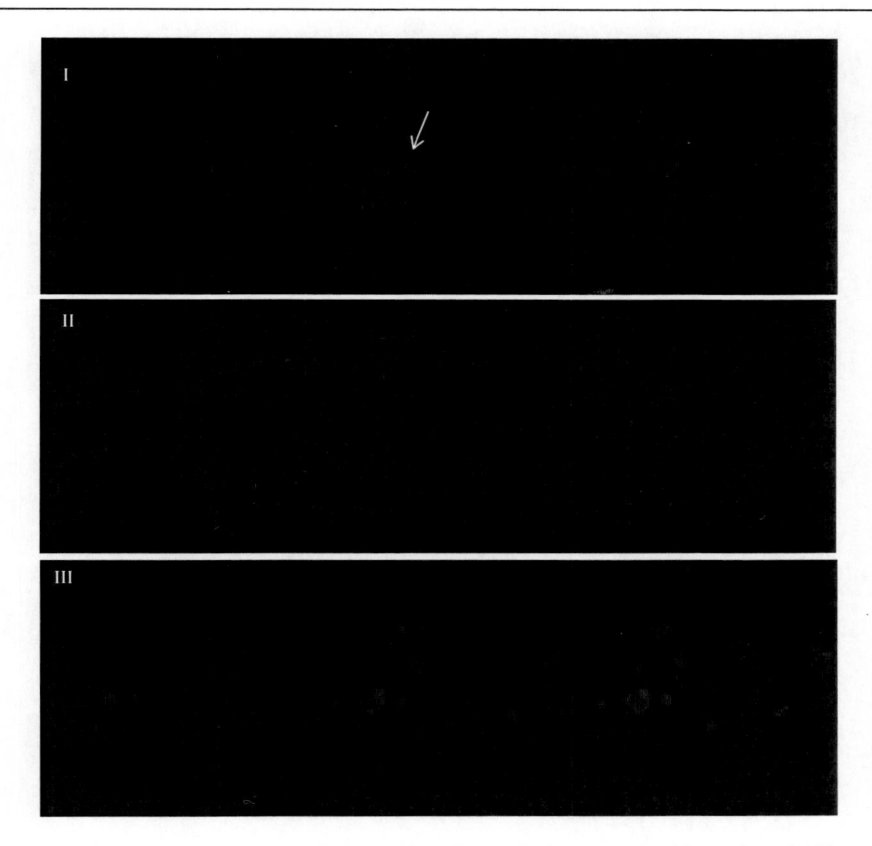

Figure 5. Confocal microscopy images of MCF7 cells incubated with (I) free CAlPc, (II) liposomal formulation containing ClAlPc, and (III) liposomal formulation containing both ClAlPc and folic acid. In the first column, the blue color shows cell nuclei marked with DAPI; in the second column, the red color results from intracellular ClAlPc fluorescence emission and in the third column, the images are superimposed.

In both cases (HaCat and MCF7), the PS drug accumulates in the cytoplasm. This agrees with the fact that PS drugs preferentially accumulate in organelles such as lysosomes and mitochondria (Barbugli, P. A., 2010). This also corroborates well with cellular internalization profile proposed for liposomes – lysosomes act on endocytosed liposomes, releasing the drug (Duzgunes & Nir, 1999; Almofti et al., 2003; Simões et al., 2001).

The region indicated by the arrow in image I of Figures 5 and 6 shows that the PS drug also seems to be around the cytoplasm. Therefore, full internalization did not occur, evidencing that the liposome (pictures II and III) facilitated intracellular drug delivery in cancer cells, as expected.

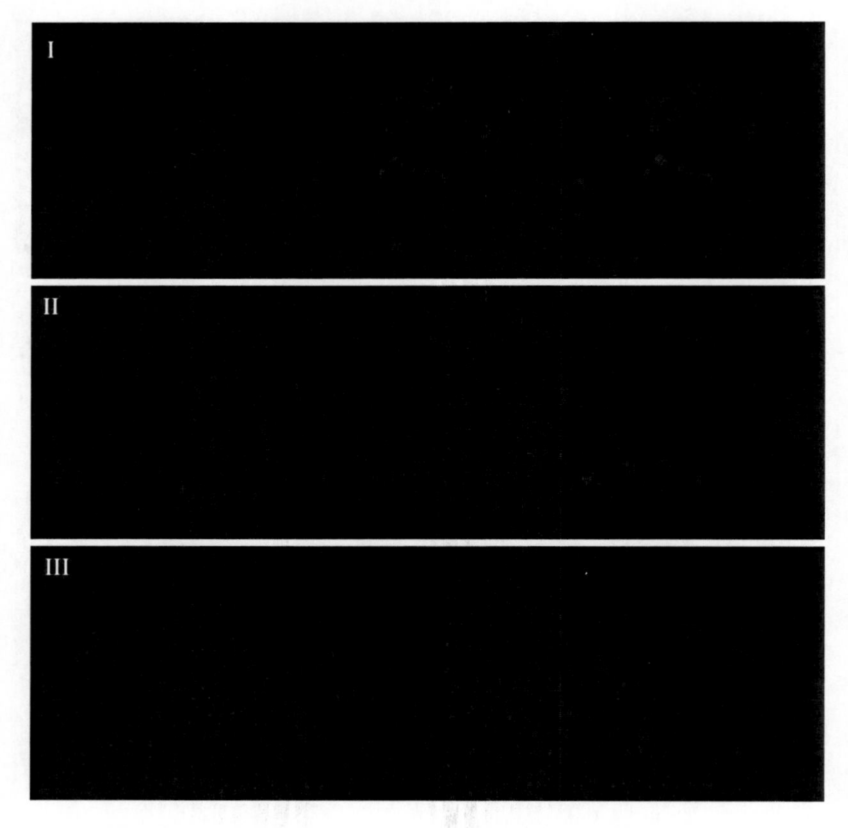

Figure 6. Confocal microscopy images of HaCat cells incubated with (I) free CAlPc, (II) liposomal formulation containing ClAlPc, and (III) liposomal formulation containing both ClAlPc and folic acid. In the first column, the blue color shows cell nuclei marked with DAPI; in the second column, the red color results from intracellular ClAlPc fluorescence emission and in the third column, the images are superimposed.

To analyze intracellular ClAlPc fluorescence emission, we seeded the HaCat and MCF7 cells (2 x 10^5 cells/well) in 24-well plates. After 24h, we incubated the cells (37 ^{o}C and 5% CO2) with formulations the PS drug a concentration of 0.5 mol/L^{-1} and then washed them with Hank's buffer to remove the PS drug that did not internalize in the cells. We measured fluorescence emission using an ELISA spectrophotometer (Safire2 - Tekan); we recorded spectra from 650 to 800 nm at an excitation wavelength of 615 nm, directly on the culture plate.

We analyzed the data provided by the software Magellan5 installed in the spectrophotometer for each well of cells treated with the formulations and compared them with the spectroscopic data obtained by directly measuring of the fluorescence emission of the liposome containing ClAlPc in the same equipment and conditions. Therefore, we considered that the fluorescence emission of the liposome containing ClAlPc was 100% at 680 nm. We used the software GraphPad Prism 3 to process the data. We determined the statistical significance of the differences between results using One-way analysis of variance (ANOVA) followed by Tukey's post-test for multiple comparisons (* $p < 0.05$).

The ClAlPc fluorescence emission enabled us to evaluate the difference between the internalization of the liposomal formulations. Addition of folic acid to the liposomal system containing ClAlPc promoted better PS drug intracellular delivery (20% higher delivery, Figure 7). PS drug delivery was greater in cancer cells (MCF7) as compared with healthy cells (HaCat).

As previously mentioned endocytosis is, the primary route through which the enters the cell liposome. Therefore, a connection must exist between a ligand and a receptor present on the cell membrane, followed by inward cell membrane folding. This will form an intracellular vesicle, called endosome, which will be released into the cytoplasm (Leamon & Low, 1992). This endocytosis may be more effective in the presence of a specific receptor, such as the folate receptor.

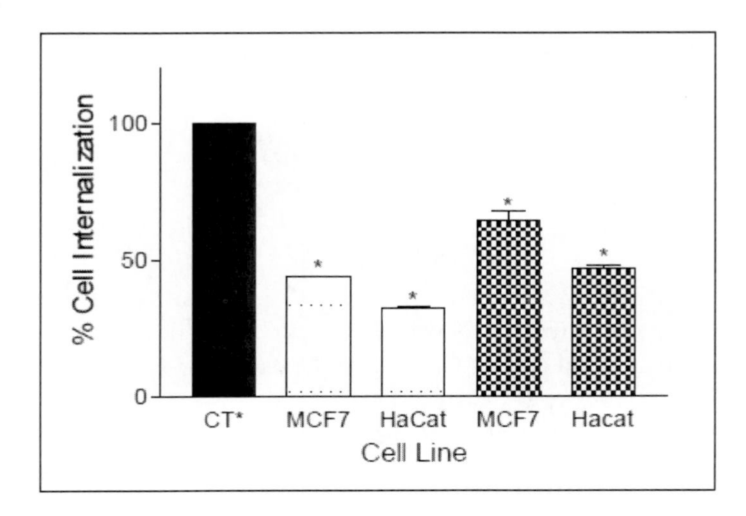

Figure 7. Percent of liposomal formulation internalized in HaCat and MCF7 cells after 3h of incubation. corresponds to the liposome containing ClAlPc and corresponds to the liposome containing ClAlPc and folic acid. Statistical significance compared with the control (* $p < 0.05$).

Folate derivatives enter the cells through facilitated transport by a membrane transport protein, the reduced folate carrier (Ke , Mathias & GREEN, 2003), this protein is highly expressed in human cancer cells (Sudimack & Lee, 2000). This accounts for the greater PS drug internalization in MCF7 cells, especially the liposomal formulation contains folic acid.

In summary, we have described the synthesis of a new liposomal system containing the effective PS drug ClAlPc and the active targeting agent folic acid. This system combined the advantages of nanotechnology PDT at low light doses to promote PS drug cell internalization, to treat brast cancer *in vitro*. This will allow researchers to develop new protocols for further *in vivo* studies. Liposomal systems constitute promising systems to treat cancer has been studied (Akamatsu, 2009; Nakamura et al., 2013; Siddikuzzaman & Grace, 2012; Wang et al., 2010; Yang et al., 2011; Bolfarini et al., 2014; Zhang et al., 2013; Shaikh et al.; Hatziantoniou et al., 2006; Park et al., 2013; Tagami et al., 2012): they increase drug therapeutic effectiveness, are biocompatible and little toxic, and selectively accumulate in tissues. Moreover, their longer circulation in the body protects the drug from immune response and improves delivery at the target site. Finally, their amphiphilic character allows one to use the same formulation to carry hydrophilic and hydrophobic substances (Barbugli et al., 2010; Fan et al., 2013; Gabizon, 1995; Kaye & Richardson, 1979; Oku, 1991; Yang et al., 2011). In conclusion, liposomes are attractive to develop various *in vitro* and *in vivo* protocols to investigate anticancer therapy and treatment of other pathologies.

REFERENCES

Agostinis, P.; Berg, K.; Cengel, K. A.; Foster, T. H.; Girotti, A. W.; Gollnick, S. O.; Hahn, S. M.; Hamblin, M. R.; Juzeniene, A.; Kessel, D.; Korbelik, M.; Moan, J.; Mroz, P.; Nowis, D.; Piette, J.; Wilson, B. C.; Golab, J. Photodynamic Therapy of Cancer: An Update, *CA: A Cancer Journal for Clinicians*, v. 61, p. 250-281, 2011.

Akamatsu, K. Development of a thermal neutron-sensitive liposome for a novel drug delivery system aiming for radio-chemo-concurrent cancer therapy, *Radiation Physics and Chemistry*, v. 78, p. 1179-1183, 2009.

Ally, J.; Martin, B.; Behrad Khamesee, M.; Roa, W.; Amirfazli, A. Magnetic targeting of aerosol particles for cancer therapy, *Journal of Magnetism and Magnetic Materials*, v. 293, p. 442-449, 2005.

Almofti, R. M.; Harashima, H.; Shinohara, Y.; Almofti, A.; Baba, Y.; Kiwada, H. Cationic liposome-mediated gene delivery: Biophysical study and mechanism of internalization, *Archives of Biochemistry and Biophysics*, v. 410, p. 246-253, 2003.

Asai, T. Nanoparticle-Mediated Delivery of Anticancer Agents to Tumor Angiogenic Vessels, *Biological & Pharmaceutical Bulletin*, v. 35, p. 1855-1861, 2012.

Barbugli, P. A. Estudo dos efeitos da terapia fotodinâmica na progressão tumoral e em modelos celulares tridimensionais. 2010. Tese (Doutorado em Medicamentos e Cosméticos) - Faculdade de Ciências Farmacêuticas de Ribeirão Preto, Universidade de São Paulo, Ribeirão Preto,2010.

Barbugli, P. A.; Siqueira-Moura, M. P.; Espreafico, E. M.; Tedesco, A. C. In Vitro Phototoxicity of Liposomes and Nanocapsules Containing Chloroaluminum Phthalocyanine on Human Melanoma Cell Line, *Journal of Nanoscience and Nanotechnology*, v. 10, p. 569-573, 2010.

Batista, C. M.; Carvalho, C. M. B. d.; Magalhães, N. S. S. Lipossomas e suas aplicações terapêuticas: estado da arte, *Revista Brasileira de Ciências Farmacêuticas*, v. 43, p. 167-179, 2007.

Bednarski, P. J.; Mackay, F. S.; Sadler, P. J. Photoactivatable Platinum Complexes. *Anti-Cancer Agents in Medicinal Chemistry,* v. 7, p. 75-93, 2007.

Bisby, R. H.; Mead, C.; Morgan, C. G. Active uptake of drugs into photosensitive liposomes and rapid release on UV photolysis. *Photochemistry and Photobiology*, v. 72, p. 57-61, 2000.

Bolfarini, G. C.; Siqueira-Moura, M. P.; Demets, G. J. F.; Morais, P. C.; Tedesco, A. C. In vitro evaluation of combined hyperthermia and photodynamic effects using magnetoliposomes loaded with cucurbituril zinc phthalocyanine complex on melanoma, *Journal of Photochemistry and Photobiology B: Biology*, v. 115, p. 1-4, 2012.

Bolfarini, G. C.; Siqueira-Moura, M. P.; Demets, G. J. F.; Tedesco, A. C. Preparation, characterization, and in-ávitro phototoxic effect of zinc phthalocyanine cucurbit[7]uril complex encapsulated into liposomes, *Dyes and Pigments*, v. 100, p. 162-167, 2014.

Bonnett, R. *Chemical Aspects of Photodinamic Therapy - Chlorins and Bacteriochlorins.* In: ADVANCED CHEMISTRY TEXTS. Chemical Aspects of Photodynamic Therapy. London: Gordon and Breach Science Publischers, 2000. Capítulo 9, p. 176-197.

Cairns, R. A.; Harris, I. S.; Mak, T. W. Regulation of cancer cell metabolism, *Nature Reviews Cancer*, v. 11, p. 85-95, 2011.

Chen, C.; Han, D.; Cai, C.; Tang, X. An overview of liposome lyophilization and its future potential, *Journal of Controlled Release*, v. 142, p. 299-311, 2010.

Cho, K.; Wang, X.; Nie, S.; Chen, Z.; Shin, D. M. Therapeutic Nanoparticles for Drug Delivery in Cancer, *Clinical Cancer Research*, v. 14, p. 1310-1316, 2008.

Compagnin, C.; Mognato, M.; Celotti, L.; Canti, G.; Palumbo, G.; Reddi, G. Cell proliferation and cell cycle alterations in oesophageal p53-mutated cancer cells treated with cisplatin in combination with photodynamic therapy. *Cell Proliferation*, v. 43, p. 263-274, 2010.

Davis, M.E.; Chen, Z.; Shin, D.M. Nanoparticle therapeutics: an emerging treatment modality for cancer, *Nature Reviews*, v.7, p. 771-782, 2008.

De Paula, C. S.; Tedesco, A. C.; Primo, F. L.; Vilela, J. M. C.; Andrade, M. S.; Mosqueira, V. C. F. Chloroaluminium phthalocyanine polymeric nanoparticles as photosensitisers: Photophysical and physicochemical characterisation, release and phototoxicity in vitro, *European Journal of Pharmaceutical Sciences*, v. 49, p. 371-381, 2013.

De Paula, L. B.; Primo, F. L.; Jardim, D. R.; Morais, P. C.; Tedesco, A. C. Development, characterization, and in vitro trials of chloroaluminum phthalocyanine-magnetic nanoemulsion to hyperthermia and photodynamic therapies on glioblastoma as a biological model, *Journal of Applied Physics*, v. 111, 2012.

Derosa, M. C.; Crutchley, R. J. Photosensitized singlet oxygen and its applications, *Coordination Chemistry Reviews*, v. 233GÇô234, p. 351-371, 2002.

Derycke, A. S. L.; De Witte, P. A. M. Liposomes for photodynamic therapy, *Advanced Drug Delivery Reviews*, v. 56, p. 17-30, 2004.

Dougherty, T. J.; Gomer, C. J.; Andreson, B. W.; Jori, G.; Kessel, D.; Korbelik, J. M.; Peng, Q. Photodynamic Therapy, *Journal of the National Cancer Institute*, v. 90, p. 889-905, 1998.

Drummond, D.C.; Meyer, O.; Hong, K.; Kirpotin, D.B.; Papahadjopoulos, D. Optimizing Liposomes for Delivery of Chemotherapeutic Agents to Solid Tumors, *Pharmacological Reviews*, v.51, p.691-743, 1999.

Duzgunes, N.; Nir, S. Mechanisms and kinetics of liposome-cell interactions, *Advanced Drug Delivery Reviews*, v. 40, p. 3-18, 1999.

Fan, Y.; Liu, J.; Wang, D.; Song, X.; Hu, Y.; Zhang, C.; Zhao, X.; Nguyen, T. L. The preparation optimization and immune effect of epimedium polysaccharide-propolis flavone liposome, *Carbohydrate Polymers*, v. 94, p. 24-30, 2013.

Gabizon, A. A. Liposome circulation time and tumor targeting: implications for cancer chemotherapy, *Advanced Drug Delivery Reviews*, v. 16, p. 285-294, 1995.

Gao, Z.; Zhang, L.; Sun, Y. Nanotechnology applied to overcome tumor drug resistance, *Journal of Controlled Release*, v.162, p. 45-55, 2012.

Gregoriadis, G. *Liposome technology: Preparation of liposomes* Boca Raton: 1984.

Harashima, H.; Kiwada, H. Liposomal targeting and drug delivery: kinetic consideration, *Advanced Drug Delivery Reviews*, v. 19, p. 425-444, 1996.

Hatziantoniou, S.; Dimas, K.; Georgopoulos, A.; Sotiriadou, N.; Demetzos, C. Cytotoxic and antitumor activity of liposome-incorporated sclareol against cancer cell lines and human colon cancer xenografts, *Pharmacological Research*, v. 53, p. 80-87, 2006.

Hayashi, K.; Shimanouchi, T.; Kato, K.; Miyazaki, T.; Nakamura, A.; Umakoshi, H. Span 80 vesicles have a more fluid, flexible and "wet" surface than phospholipid liposomes, *Colloids and Surfaces B-Biointerfaces*, v. 87, p. 28-35, 2011.

Hoebeke, M. *The importance of liposomes as models and tools in the understanding of photosensitization mechanisms*, *Journal of Photochemistry and Photobiology B: Biology*, v. 28, p. 189-196, 1995.

Jackson, J. K.; Pirmoradi, F. N.; Wan, C. P. L.; Siu, T.; Chiao, M.; Burt, H. M. Increased accumulation of paclitaxel and doxorubicin in proliferating capillary cells and prostate cancer cells following ultrasound exposure, *Ultrasonics*, v. 51, p. 932-939, 2011.

Jori, G. *Tumour photosensitizers: approaches to enhance the selectivity and efficiency of photodynamic therapy*, *Journal of Photochemistry and Photobiology B: Biology*, v. 36, p. 87-93, 1996.

Kaye, S.; Richardson, V. J. *Potential of liposomes as drug carriers in cancer chemotherapy: a review*, *Cancer Chemotherapy Pharmacological*, v. 3, p. 81-85, 1979.

Ke, C. Y.; Mathias, C. J.; Green, M. A. The folate receptor as a molecular target for tumor-selective radionuclide delivery, *Nuclear Medicine and Biology*, v. 30, p. 811-817, 2003.

Kelley, K. M.; Rowan, B. G.; Ratnam, M. Modulation of the folate receptor alpha gene by the estrogen receptor: mechanism and implications in tumor targeting, *Cancer research*, v. 63, p. 2820-2828, 2003.

Konishi, M.; Tabata, Y.; Kariya, M.; Suzuki, A.; Mandai, M.; Nanbu, K.; Takakura, K.; Fujii, S. In vivo anti-tumor effect through the controlled release of cisplatin from biodegradable gelatin hydrogel. *Journal of Controlled Release*, v. 92, p. 301-313, 2003.

Laouini, A.; Jaafar-Maalej, C.; Sfar, S.; Charcosset, C.; Fessi, H. Liposome preparation using a hollow fiber membrane contactor-Application to spironolactone encapsulation, *International Journal of Pharmaceutics*, v. 415, p. 53-61, 2011.

Leamon, C. P.; Low, P. S. Cytotoxicity of momordin-folate conjugates in cultured human cells, *The Journal of Biological Chemistry*, v. 267, p. 24966-24971, 1992.

Li, A. S.; Chignell, C. F. Spectroscopic studies of cutaneous photosensitizing agents--IX. A spin trapping study of the photolysis of amiodarone and desethylamiodarone, *Photochemistry and Photobiology*, v. 45, p. 191-197, 1987

Liang, C. Y.; Yang, Y. B.; Ling, Y.; Huang, Y. S.; Li, T.; Li, X. M. Improved therapeutic effect of folate-decorated PLGA-PEG nanoparticles for endometrial carcinoma, *Bioorganic & Medicinal Chemistry*, v. 19, p. 4057-4066, 2011.

Liu, Y. T.; Li, K.; Pan, J.; Liu, B.; Feng, S. S. Folic acid conjugated nanoparticles of mixed lipid monolayer shell and biodegradable polymer core for targeted delivery of Docetaxel, *Biomaterials*, v. 31, p. 330-338, 2010.

London, E. Lipid Bilayer Structure. In: EDITORS-IN-CHIEF: WILLIAM, J. L., LANE, M. D. Encyclopedia of Biological Chemistry. Waltham: Academic Press, 2013. p. 733-735.

Longo J. P.; Melo, L. N. D.; Mijan,M. C.; Valois, C. R. A.; Joanitti, G. A.; Simioni, A. R., Tedesco, A. C.; Azevedo, R. B. Photodynamic Therapy Mediated by Liposomal Chloroaluminum-Phthalocyanine Induces Necrosis in Oral Cancer Cells. *Journal of Biomaterials and Tissue Engineering* 2013. 1: 148-56.

Lu, B.; Xiong, S. B.; Yang, H.; Yin, X. D.; Zhao, R. B. Mitoxantrone-loaded BSA nanospheres and chitosan nanospheres for local injection against breast cancer and its lymph node metastases: II: Tissue distribution and pharmacodynamics, *International Journal of Pharmaceutics*, v. 307, p. 175-181, 2006.

Luo, Y.; Kessel, D. Initiation of apoptpsis versus necrosis by photodynamic therapy with cloroaluminum phtalocyanine, Journal of Photochemistry and Photobiology, v.66, p.479, 1997.

Lv, Q.; Li, L. M.; Han, M.; Tang, X. J.; Yao, J. N.; Ying, X. Y.; Li, F. Z.; Gao, J. Q. Characteristics of sequential targeting of brain glioma for transferrin-modified cisplatin liposome, *International Journal of Pharmaceutics*, v. 444, p. 1-9, 2013.

Maherani, B.; Arab-Tehrany, E.; Kheirolomoom, A.; Cleymand, F.; Linder, M. Influence of lipid composition on physicochemical properties of nanoliposomes encapsulating natural dipeptide antioxidant l-carnosine, *Food Chemistry*, v. 134, p. 632-640, 2012.

Maranho, D. S.; De Lima, R. G.; Primo, F. L.; Da Silva, R. S.; Tedesco, A. C. Photoinduced Nitric Oxide and Singlet Oxygen Release from ZnPC Liposome Vehicle Associated with the Nitrosyl Ruthenium Complex: Synergistic Effects in Photodynamic Therapy Application, *Photochemistry and Photobiology*, v. 85, p. 705-713, 2009.

Ministério da Saúde; INCA, Instituto Nacional do Câncer. ABC do Câncer: Abordagens Básicas para o Controle do Câncer [online]. 2011. Available from: http://bvsms.saude.gov.br/bvs/publicacoes/abc_do_cancer.pdf

Molinari, A.; Colone, M.; Calcabrini, A.; Stringaro, A.; Toccacieli, L.; Arancia, G.; Mannino, S.; Mangiola, A.; Maira, G.; Bombelli, C.; Mancini, G. Cationic liposomes, loaded with m-THPC, in photodynamic therapy for malignant glioma, *Toxicology in Vitro*, v. 21, p. 230-234, 2007.

Morgan, J.; Jackson, J.D.; Zheng, X.; Pandey, S.K.; Pandey, R.K. Substrate affinity of photosensitizers derived from chorophyll-a: The ABCG2 transporter affects the phototoxic response of side population stem cell-like cancer cells to photodynamic tehrapy, *Molecular Pharmacology,* v.7, p. 1789-1804, 2010.

Nakamura, T.; Yamazaki, D.; Yamauchi, J.; Harashima, H. The nanoparticulation by octaarginine-modified liposome improves a-galactosylceramide-mediated antitumor therapy via systemic administration, *Journal of Controlled Release*, v. 171, p. 216-224, 2013.

Nguyen, D. X.; Bos, P. D.; Massague, J. Metastasis: from dissemination to organ-specific colonization, *Nature Reviews Cancer*, v. 9, p. 274-284, 2009.

Niziolek, M.; Korytowski, W.; Girotti, A. W. Nitric oxide inhibition of free radical-mediated lipid peroxidation in photodynamically treated membranes and cells. *Free Radical Biology and Medicine*, v. 34, p. 997-1005, 2003.

Nombona, N.; Maduray, K.; Antunes, E.; Karsten, A.; Nyokong, T. Synthesis of phthalocyanine conjugates with gold nanoparticles and liposomes for photodynamic therapy, *Journal of Photochemistry and Photobiology B: Biology*, v. 107, p. 35-44, 2012.

Nunes, S. M. T.; Sguilaa,F. S.; Tedesco, A. C. Photophysical studies of zinc phthalocyanine and chloroaluminium phtalocyanine incorporated into liposomes in the presence of additives., *Brazilian Journal of Medical and Biology Research* 2004.

Nunes, S. M. *A Potencialidade do uso de diferentes sistemas de liberação de farmacos na Terapia Fotodinamica: preparação e estudos fotofisicos.* 2003. Faculdade de Filosofia Ciencias e Letras de Ribeirão Preto-USP,2003.

Oku, N. *Lipossomes.* In: Dunn, R., Ottenbrit, R. Polimeric drugs and drug delivery systems. ACS Symposium Series, 1991. p. 24-33.

Oyarzun-Ampuero, F. A.; Rivera-Rodriguez, G. R.; Alonso, M. J.; Torres, D. Hyaluronan nanocapsules as a new vehicle for intracellular drug delivery, *European Journal of Pharmaceutical Sciences*, v. 49, p. 483-490, 2013.

Park, S. M.; Kim, M. S.; Park, S. J.; Park, E. S.; Choi, K. S.; Kim, Y. S.; Kim, H. R. Novel temperature-triggered liposome with high stability: Formulation, in vitro evaluation, and in vivo study combined with high-intensity focused ultrasound (HIFU), *Journal of Controlled Release*, v. 170, p. 373-379, 2013.

Paszko, E.; Ehrhardtb, C.; Senge, M. O.; Kelleher, D. P.; Reynolds, J. V. Nanodrug applications in photodynamic therapy, *Photodiagnosis and Photodynamic Therapy* 2010.

Paiva, M. B.; Joo, J.; Abrahao, M.; Ribeiro, J. C.; Cervantes, O.; Sercarz, J. A. Update on Laser Photochemotherapy: An Alternative for Cancer Treatment. *Anti-Cancer Agents in Medicinal Chemistry*, v. 11, p. 772-779, 2011.

Peng, C. Y.; Zhang, Y. Y.; Tong, W. J.; Gao, C. Y. influence of Folate Conjugation on the Cellular Uptake Degree of Poly(allylamine hydrochloride) Microcapsules, *Journal of Applied Polymer Science*, v. 121, p. 3710-3716, 2011.

Petrak, K. Essential properties of drug-targeting delivery systems, *Drug Discovery Today*, v. 10, p. 1667-1673, 2005.

Primo, F. L. Processos fotodinâmicos para bioestimulação tecidual em modelo *in vitro* de pele humana empregando-se laser de baixa potência e cloro alumínio ftalocianina em nanoemulsão. 2009. 195 f. Tese (Doutorado em Medicamentos e Cosméticos) - Faculdade de Ciências Farmacêuticas de Ribeirão Preto, Universidade de São Paulo, Ribeirão Preto,2009.

Primo, F. L.; Bentley, M. V. L. B.; Tedesco, A. C. Photophysical studies and in vitro skin permeation/retention of Foscan (R)/nanoemulsion (NE) applicable to photodynamic therapy skin cancer treatment, *Journal of Nanoscience and Nanotechnology*, v. 8, p. 340-347, 2008.

Primo, F. L.; Rodrigues, M. M. A.; Simioni, A. R.; Bentley, M. V. L. B.; Morais, P. C.; Tedesco, A. C. In vitro studies of cutaneous retention of magnetic nanoemulsion loaded with zinc phthalocyanine for synergic use in skin cancer treatment, *Journal of Magnetism and Magnetic Materials*, v. 320, p. E211-E214, 2008.

Primo, F. L.; Siqueira-Moura, M. P.; Simioni, A. R.; Peti, A. P. F.; Tedesco, A. C. Preparation, characterization and citotoxicity assays of chloroaluminum phthalocyanine photosensitizer drug loaded in PLGA-nanocapsules, *Drugs of the Future*, v. 32, p. 74, 2007.

Ricchelli, F. Photophysical properties of porphyrins in biological membranes, *Journal of Photochemistry and Photobiology B: Biology*, v. 29, p. 109-118, 1995.

Robertson, C.A., Hawkins Evans, D.; Abrahamse, H. Photodinamic therapy (PDT): a short review on cellular mechanisms and cancer research applications for PDT. *Journal of Photochemistry and Photobiology: B*, v. 96, p. 1-8, 2009.

Santos, N. C.; Castanho, M. A. R. B. Lipossomas: a bala magica acertou?, *Química Nova*, v. 25, p. 1181-1185, 2002.

Schmid, M. H.; Korting, H. C. Therapeutic progress with topical liposome drugs for skin disease, *Advanced Drug Delivery Reviews*, v. 18, p. 335-342, 1996.

Shaikh, I. M.; Tan, K. B.; Chaudhury, A.; Liu, Y.; Tan, B. J.; Tan, B. M. J.; Chiu, G. N. C. Liposome co-encapsulation of synergistic combination of irinotecan and doxorubicin for the treatment of intraperitoneally grown ovarian tumor xenograft, *Journal of Controlled Release*.

Shen, Z.; LI, Y.; Kohama, K.; Oneill, B.; BI, J. Improved drug targeting of cancer cells by utilizing actively targetable folic acid-conjugated albumin nanospheres, *Pharmacological Research*, v. 63, p. 51-58, 2011.

Siddikuzzaman; Grace, V. M. B. Inhibition of metastatic lung cancer in C57BL/6 mice by liposome encapsulated all trans retinoic acid (ATRA), *International Immunopharmacology*, v. 14, p. 570-579, 2012.

Simioni, A. R.; Pelisson, M. M. M.; Beltrame JR, M.; Tedesco, A. C. Photophysical and Photobiological Studies of a Silicon Tribenzonaphthoporphyrazinato Incorporated into Liposomes for Photodynamic Therapy Use, *Journal of Nanoscience and Nanotechnology*, v. 8, p. 3208-3215, 2008.

Simioni, A. R.; Primo, F. L.; Rodrigues, M. M. A.; Lacava, Z. G. M.; Morais, P. C.; Tedesco, A. C. Preparation, characterization and in vitro toxicity test of magnetic nanoparticle-based drug delivery system to hyperthermia of biological tissues, *Ieee Transactions on Magnetics*, v. 43, p. 2459-2461, 2007.

Simioni, A. R.; Rodrigues, M. M. A.; Primo, F. L.; Morais, P. C.; Tedesco, A. C. Effect of Diode-Laser and AC Magnetic Field of Bovine Serum Albumin Nanospheres Loaded with Phthalocyanine and Magnetic Particles, *Journal of Nanoscience and Nanotechnology*, v. 11, p. 3604-3608, 2011.

Simões, S.; Slepushkin, V.; Duzgunes, N.; Pedroso De Lima, M. C. On the mechanisms of internalization and intracellular delivery mediated by pH-sensitive liposomes, *Biochimica et Biophysica Acta (BBA) - Biomembranes*, v. 1515, p. 23-37, 2001.

Siqueira-Moura, M. P.; Primo, F. L.; Espreafico, E. M.; Tedesco, A. C. Development, characterization, and photocytotoxicity assessment on human melanoma of chloroaluminum phthalocyanine nanocapsules, *Materials Science and Engineering: C*, v. 33, p. 1744-1752, 2013.

Sobolev, A.; Jans, D.; Rosenkranz, A. *Targeted entracellular delivery of photosensitizers*, *Progress in Biophysics & Molecular Biology*, v. 73, p. 51-90, 2000.

Sudimack, J.; Lee, R. J. Targeted drug delivery via the folate receptor, *Advanced Drug Delivery Reviews*, v. 41, p. 147-162, 2000.

Suzuki, H.; Nakai, D.; Seita, T.; Sugiyama, Y. Design of a drug delivery system for targeting based on pharmacokinetic consideration, *Advanced Drug Delivery Reviews*, v. 19, p. 335-357, 1996.

Tagami, T.; Suzuki, T.; Matsunaga, M.; Nakamura, K.; Moriyoshi, N.; Ishida, T.; Kiwada, H. Anti-angiogenic therapy via cationic liposome-mediated systemic siRNA delivery, *International Journal of Pharmaceutics*, v. 422, p. 280-289, 2012.

Triesscheijn, M.; Baas, P.; Schellens, J. H. M.; Stewart, F. A. Photodynamic Therapy in Oncology, *The Oncologist*, v. 11, p. 1034-1044, 2006.

Valencia, P. M.; Hanewich-Hollatz, M. H.; Gao, W. W.; Karim, F.; Langer, R.; Karnik, R.; Farokhzad, O. C. Effects of ligands with different water solubilities on self-assembly and properties of targeted nanoparticles, *Biomaterials*, v. 32, p. 6226-6233, 2011.

Vemuri, S.; Rhodes, C. *Preparation and characterization of liposomes as therapeutic delivery systems: a review*, *Pharmaceutica Acta Helvetiae,* v. 70, p. 95-111, 1995.

Vergara, D.; Bellomo, C.; Zhang, X.; Vergaro, V.; Tinelli, A.; Lorusso, V.; Rinaldi, R.; Lvov, Y. M.; Leporatti, S.; Maffia, M. Lapatinib/Paclitaxel polyelectrolyte nanocapsules for overcoming multidrug resistance in ovarian cancer, *Nanomedicine: Nanotechnology, Biology and Medicine*, v. 8, p. 891-899, 2012.

Wang, X.; Zhou, J.; Wang, Y.; Zhu, Z.; Lu, Y.; Wei, Y.; Chen, L. A phase I clinical and pharmacokinetic study of paclitaxel liposome infused in non-small cell lung cancer patients with malignant pleural effusions, *European Journal of Cancer*, v. 46, p. 1474-1480, 2010.

Wongsagonsup, R.; Shobsngob, S.; Oonkhanond, B.; Varavinit, S. Zeta Potential (ζ) Analysis for the Determination of Protein Content in Rice Flour. *Starch/Stärke*. v.57, p. 25-31, 2005.

Woodle, M. C. Sterically stabilized liposome therapeutics, *Advanced Drug Delivery Reviews*, v. 16, p. 249-265, 1995.

Yang, F.; Jin, C.; Jiang, Y.; Li, J.; Di, Y.; Ni, Q.; Fu, D. Liposome based delivery systems in pancreatic cancer treatment: From bench to bedside, *Cancer Treatment Reviews*, v. 37, p. 633-642, 2011.

Zenkevich, E.; Sagun, E.; Knyukshto, V.; Shulga, A.; Mironov, A.; Efremova, O.; Bonnett, R.; Songca, S. P.; Kassem, M. Photophysical and photochemical properties of potential porphyrin and chlorin photosensitizers for PDT, *Journal of Photochemistry and Photobiology B: Biology*, v. 33, p. 171-180, 1996.

Zhang, J.; Tian, H.; Li, C.; Cheng, L.; Zhang, S.; Zhang, X.; Wang, R.; Xu, F.; Dai, L.; Shi, G.; Chen, X.; Li, Y.; Du, T.; Deng, J.; Liu, Y.; Yang, Y.; Wei, Y.; Deng, H. Antitumor effects obtained by autologous Lewis lung cancer cell vaccine engineered to secrete mouse Interleukin 27 by means of cationic liposome, *Molecular Immunology*, v. 55, p. 264-274, 2013.

Zhou, C. Mechanisms of tumor necrosis induced by photodynamic therapy, *Journal of Photochemistry and Photobiology B: Biology*, v. 3, p. 299-318, 1989.

In: Advances in Liposomes Research
Editor: Lauren Finney
ISBN: 978-1-63117-074-4

Chapter 5

LIPOSOME APPLICATIONS IN THE VETERINARY FIELD

Monica Florin-Christensen**, Anabel E. Rodriguez, Mariela L. Tomazic and Leonhard Schnittger

Instituto de Patobiologia, Centro de Investigaciones en Ciencias Veterinarias y Agronomicas (CICVyA), INTA-Castelar, Hurlingham; and Consejo Nacional de Investigaciones Cientificas y Tecnicas (CONICET), Buenos Aires, Argentina

ABSTRACT

In the field of veterinary medicine, liposomes are the most widespread nanotechnological tool. Already for some time, they have been applied in animal therapies to improve delivery of different drugs, comprising analgesic, antiviral, antimicrobial, antifungal, and anticancer agents. More recently, with the rise of recombinant DNA technologies, liposomes have been included in veterinary vaccine formulations to entrap antigen-coding DNAs, siRNAs, peptides, and recombinant antigens, as well as effectors of the innate immune system, in order to elicit protective responses against viruses, bacteria and parasites. Reported applications include their use in companion and productive animals, among others horse, dog, cattle, poultry, and fish. Liposomes are

* Corresponding author: Monica Florin-Christensen, Ph.D. Instituto de Patobiologia, CICVyA, INTA-Castelar, Los Reseros y Nicolas Repetto, s/n, 1686 Hurlingham, Provincia de Buenos Aires, Argentina, Phone: +54 11 621 1289, ext. 145, Email: mflorin@cnia.inta.gov.ar.

generally well tolerated and, in accordance with their purpose, may be delivered through the intramuscular, subcutaneous, intravenous, ocular, and/or intranasal route to their desired target. In order to achieve a more specific tissue targeting, engineering of liposomes has also been described in the veterinary field. Besides therapeutics, liposomes have also been applied in transfection technologies and in the cryopreservation of stallion or bull semen. Use of liposomes can be limited by the high manufacturing costs of lipid synthesis or purification. Therefore, the formulation of low-cost liposomes made of non-purified lipid mixtures will open the possibility of large-scale applications in animal productive systems. This chapter presents an overview on possibilities, advantages, and perspectives of liposome employment for veterinary use.

1. INTRODUCTION

Liposomes were discovered by Bangham and Home (1964) who observed under the electron microscope that "spherulites composed of concentric lamellae" were formed when lecithin was dispersed in an aqueous solution. These structures were at first referred to as "multilamellar smectic mesophases", "phospholipid spherules", or, less seriously, "banghasomes" (Deamer, 2010), but the more appealing term of "liposomes", derived from the two Greek words *lipo* (fat) and *soma* (body), was soon after suggested and widely accepted (Sessa & Weissmann,1968; Deamer, 2010).

Since liposomes were found to share a number of features with natural membrane-bounded structures, such as ion discrimination, osmotic swelling and response to a variety of physiologic and pharmacologic agents, they were proposed as a valuable model system to study lipid-dependent properties of biological membranes (Sessa & Weissmann, 1968).

Soon after, Gregoriadis et al. (1971) envisioned their use in medicine as a delivery system of enzymes for human patients with storage diseases, i.e. absence or low production of a particular enzyme with the consequent accumulation of certain non-desired molecules. Reduction of immunological reactions of the body and avoidance of the circulation of an active enzyme in the blood were good reasons to favor the use of liposome-encapsulated over non encapsulated enzymes. Additionally, experiments in rats showed that radiolabeled albumin encapsulated in liposomes was efficiently delivered to the liver and spleen, showing that liposomes could be targeted to a particular tissue. These foundational experiments opened the door to a plethora of therapeutic applications. Indeed, liposomes are nowadays one of the basic tools of nanomedicine, which has been defined by the National Institutes of Health as "an offshoot of nanotechnology, which refers to highly specific medical intervention at the molecular scale for curing disease or repairing damaged tissues, such as bone, muscle, or nerve".

Human and veterinary medicine face similar challenges and benefit from each other; the intertwining between both "medicines" becomes particularly tight when considering zoonotic diseases (Zinsstag et al., 2011). As with many other technological advances, nanotechnology has slowly invaded the veterinary medicine arena and has already provided, and will further provide, innovative solutions to several problems connected to animal health and/or production (Underwood & van Eps, 2012).

Essentially, liposomes are microscopic vesicles formed by one or more lipid bilayers (unilamellar or multilamellar liposomes, respectively). They are mainly composed of phospholipids and cholesterol and range in size from 0.02 to 2 μm. They constitute a highly versatile dispatch system for hydrophilic molecules as these are entrapped in their aqueous core, while hydrophobic molecules can be incorporated to the phospholipid lamellae. In addition, their net charge can be tailored and different natural or synthetic molecules can be covalently bound to their surface to increase the efficiency of delivery to the target (Torchilin, 2005; Immordino et al., 2006).

In the following sections, we provide examples of successful applications of liposomes to different aspects of veterinary medicine, including vaccination, drug delivery, transfection technologies, and semen cryopreservation.

2. VACCINATION

Vaccines are considered the most effective and sustainable means for disease control. Many common vaccines are still based on killed or live attenuated pathogens, though subunit formulations constitute an attractive alternative, due to their lower associated sanitary risks, improved storage, and suitability for up-scaling. Therefore, as in the prevention of human diseases, considerable research efforts are also devoted to the development of subunit vaccines in the veterinary field. Liposome technology has proved to be a useful tool for the effective delivery of different types of antigens, including proteins, DNA, and lipids. Some recent applications of liposomes in experimental vaccine formulations against viral, bacterial, protozoan, and antitumor diseases of importance to companion and/or productive animals are shown in Table 1.

Table 1. Examples of the use of liposomes in veterinary vaccine formulations

Encapsulated agent		Pathogen or disease	Host	Reference
Type	Name			
Proteins or whole cell extracts	NcAMA1	*Neospora caninum*	Cattle (mouse as model)	Zhang et al., 2010
	NcGRA7			Nishikawa et al., 2009
			Cattle	Nishimura et al., 2013
	MAP0217, MAP1508, MAP3701c, MAP3783, MAP1609c/Ag85B	*Mycobacterium avium*	Cattle	Thakur et al., 2013
	Cu-Zn SOD	*Brucella abortus*	Cattle (mouse as model)	Singha et al., 2011
	SEF 21	*Salmonella enterica*	Chicken	Pang et al., 2013
	SEF14 and SEF 21			Li et al., 2004
	A. salmonicida antigen	*Aeromonas salmonicida*	Carp	Irie et al., 2005
	VP28	White spot syndrome virus	Shrimp	Mavichak et al., 2010
	Inactivated *E. coli*	*Escherichia coli*	chicken	Yaguchi et al., 2009
Plasmids encoding vaccine antigens	MSA-2c	*Babesia bovis*	Cattle (mouse as model)	Rodriguez et al., 2013
	MAG1	*Toxoplasma gondii*	Sheep	Hiszczynska-Sawicka et al., 2010
	GRA1, GRA4, GRA6, GRA7			Hiszczynska-Sawicka et al., 2011
	MIC3			Hiszczynska-Sawicka et al., 2012
	Tax	Bovine leukaemia virus	Sheep	Usui et al., 2003
	Glycoprotein C	Anatid herpesvirus 1	Duck	Sun et al., 2013
Lipid	LPS core (Lipid A)	*Escherichia coli*	Chicken	Dissanayake et al., 2010
Adjuvants and immuno-modulators	GPSL	Newcastle disease virus	Chicken	Yu et al., 2013
	PFL			Yuan et al., 2012, 2013
	EPS			Gao et al, 2012
	GAL			Zhao et al, 2011
	EPS and PF			Fan et al., 2012
	IL-2 DNA	Chronic rhinitis	Cat	Veir et al., 2006
		Osteosarcoma	Dog	Dow et al., 2005
	Non coding plasmid DNA	Haemangiosarcoma	Dog	U'Ren et al., 2007
		Atopic dermatitis		Mueller et al., 2005
	Muramyl tripeptide	Melanoma, angiosarcoma, mammary adenocarcinoma	Cat, dog	Vail et al., 1995; Fox et al., 1995; Teske et al., 1998; MacEwen et al., 1999

An example of the usefulness of liposomes in recombinant protein-based vaccines is provided by formulations recently developed against *Neospora caninum*. This apicomplexan protozoon is a major cause of abortion in cattle provoking large direct and indirect economic loss worldwide. In order to prevent abortions and vertical transmission of the parasite, vaccine development against neosporosis is an active research field. Studies performed in a mouse model showed that vaccination with the *N. caninum* recombinant antigens NcGRA7 and NcAMA-1 encapsulated in liposomes, made of dipalmitoyl phosphatidylcholine (PC), cholesterol, and mannotriose-dipalmitoyl phosphatidylethanolamine (M3-DPPE liposomes), elicited a parasite-specific Th-1 type immune response which resulted in decreased parasite load in brains and increased offspring survival (Nishikawa et al., 2009; Zhang et al., 2010). This type of liposomes had been previously shown to have *per se* capacity of eliciting IL-12 production in macrophages (Takagi et al., 2007). Moreover, when non-pregnant cattle were subcutaneously immunized with NcGRA7 entrapped in M3-DPPE liposomes, a significantly decreased load of *N. caninum* tachyzoites was detected in brain tissues after challenge (Nishimura et al., 2013). These encouraging results show that a liposome-based approach could constitute a valid tool in the development of neosporosis vaccines for cattle.

Liposomal vaccines can be administered through different routes, according to the handling characteristics of the target species and the desired immune response type. While subcutaneous or intramuscular injection are the most common routes for vaccination of mammals with liposomal formulations, oral vaccination has proved adequate for the vaccination of aquatic animals, such as shrimp and fish. Thus, a liposomal oral vaccine was developed against white spot syndrome virus (WSSV), a pathogen with devastating effects on shrimp farms. In this formulation, multilamellar liposomes, prepared out of dioleoyl PC, dioleoyl-phosphatidylserine (PS), and cholesterol, entrapped a recombinant form of VP28, a protein component of the WSSV envelope. Shrimp fed with food pellets containing these liposomes largely survived a viral challenge, and histological observations using fluorescent markers showed that liposome-entrapped VP28 was better taken up by shrimp intestinal cells than the soluble protein alone (Mavichak et al., 2010). Also, oral administration of liposome-entrapped *Aeromonas salmonicida* antigenic preparations were successfully applied by Irie et al. (2005) to protect carp against this deadly bacterium which causes furunculosis in freshwater fish. On the other hand, the intraocular route was chosen for the administration of liposome-encapsulated *Salmonella enterica* or *Escherichia coli* antigens to chicken (Li et al., 2004; Yaguchi et al., 2009). In both cases, vaccination elicited specific mucosal and systemic immune responses which, upon challenge, significantly decreased intestine colonization by bacteria and gastroenteritis symptoms. The same effect was obtained after oral vaccination of chicken with a liposome-encapsulated *S. enterica* antigen (Pang et al., 2012).

Liposome based-formulations of experimental DNA vaccines have also been produced against a great number of important veterinary diseases. Importantly, there are licensed veterinary DNA vaccines currently available for equines against West Nile Virus, and for salmon against the Haematopoietic Necrosis Virus (Faurez et al., 2010). As with subunit formulations, DNA vaccines avoid the hazards and complications of working with living organisms as well as the risk of virulence reversion. Furthermore, due to the localization of the encoded antigens and the presence of post-translational modifications, they are likely to elicit immune responses that better mimic a natural infection than bacteria-expressed antigens (Donnelly et al., 2005).

It is believed that, upon vaccination, DNA is incorporated by muscular or other cells, followed by expression and extracellular release of the encoded antigen, which can then be taken up by antigen presenting cells (APC), eliciting cellular and humoral immune responses (Lewis & Babiuk, 1999). However, cellular uptake of naked DNA occurs with low efficiency and, in addition, DNA hydrolysis by deoxyribonucleases present in the interstitial fluids requires the injection of relatively large amounts of DNA. Liposome encapsulation of DNA can facilitate the uptake of DNA by APC and also protect it from nuclease attack, improving vaccine efficiency, as has been demonstrated in several experimental DNA formulations for veterinary use. For example, vaccination of sheep with plasmid-liposome complexes has proven suitable to elicit efficient humoral responses against various encoded *Toxoplasma gondii* antigens (Hiszczynska-Sawicka et al., 2010, 2011, 2012). Also in sheep, vaccination with liposome-encapsulated DNA encoding the Tax protein of bovine leukaemia virus (BLV) gave rise to a Th1 type immune response that inhibited BLV propagation after challenge (Usui et al., 2003). In another study, either liposomes or the cationic polymer chitosan were used to complex plasmid DNA encoding Anatid herpes virus glycoprotein C. Ducks were vaccinated with this formulation or with naked DNA, and the distribution of plasmids was analyzed in different organs. Both chitosan and liposomes similarly improved the efficiency of plasmid distribution in duck tissues, and facilitated its long-term maintenance, prerequisites to elicit an effective immune response upon vaccination (Sun et al., 2013).

Liposome encapsulation of antigenic lipids has also been used for experimental vaccine formulations and proved effective against avian colisepticemia. This kind of infection has a significant economic impact in poultry production and can be caused by 60 different *Escherichia coli* serotypes. For this reason, the level of disease control achievable with serotype-specific vaccines is limited (Parmentier et al., 2008). On the other hand, *E. coli* lipopolysaccharide (LPS) core regions, mainly composed by Lipid A, are highly immunogenic and generally conserved, but their use as poultry vaccine antigens is hampered by their toxicity as their application can lead to fever, anorexia, growth impairment, decreased respiratory capacity, and even death (Parmentier et al., 2008). Encapsulation in liposomes composed of egg PC, bovine brain PS and cholesterol has been shown to significantly reduce LPS endotoxicity. Moreover, chicken vaccinated with an appropriate dose of liposome-encapsulated LPS cores showed a clear reduction in gross lesions in the air sacs, liver and pericardial sacs upon challenge, as compared to non-vaccinated birds (Dissanayake et al., 2010). If these results are confirmed in field vaccination studies, liposomal LPS vaccines could constitute an attractive approach for the prevention of avian colisepticemia.

In addition to the right choice of antigens, adjuvants and immunomodulators are essential to trigger a protective immune response upon vaccination. Encapsulation of these agents in liposomes can improve their delivery to effector cells, as well as protect them from oxidation and/or degradation. This approach has been investigated for vaccines against Newcastle disease virus (NDV), which causes devastating loss in small and large-scale poultry production. In a series of studies carried out at Nanjing Agricultural University, China, different herbal immunomodulators, including glycyrrhetinic acid (GA), gyneposides, propolis flavonoids (PF) and epimedium polysaccharide (EPS), were encapsulated in liposomes composed of soybean phospholipids and cholesterol. These formulations were administered to chicken simultaneously with a commercially available live NDV vaccine, either orally (gyneposides) or intramuscularly (i.m; GA, PF and EPS). Noteworthy, the elicited humoral and cellular immune responses, as measured by antibody titers, lymphocyte proliferation, and cytokine production, respectively, were significantly enhanced when compared to the responses elicited by co-vaccination with the respective non-encapsulated compounds or blank liposomes (Zhao et al., 2011; Gao et al., 2012; Yuan et al., 2012, 2013; Yu et al., 2013). Moreover, in vaccination-challenge experiments, the i.m. co-injection of liposomes containing both EPS and PF significantly increased the protective activity of the NDV vaccine in chicken, as measured by morbidity and mortality rates after challenge (Fan et al., 2012). Interestingly, this combined liposome exploits the versatility of the system, since PF, a hydrophobic molecule, is contained in the lipid bilayer, while the hydrophilic EPS is encapsulated in the liposome lumen.

Non-coding plasmid DNA-liposome complexes have been shown to have potent immunostimulatory capacity and were successfully used as adjuvants in a tumor vaccine against hemangiosarcoma and an allergen-based vaccine for topical dermatitis in dogs (Mueller et al., 2005; U´Ren et al., 2007). In addition, plasmids encoding interleukin-2 have also been shown to stimulate innate immune responses and were used in liposomal formulations for immunotherapy against osteosarcoma and chronic rhinitis in dogs and cats, respectively (Dow et al., 2005; Veir et al., 2006).

In a similar way, muramyl dipeptide (MDP) is a strong immunomodulator component of bacterial cell walls. Liposomal formulations of an MDP derivative (muramyl tripeptide, MTP) have the advantages of increased stability and lower toxicity, while being similarly effective as the non-encapsulated agent in stimulating innate immune mechanisms. When macrophages and monocytes are activated by liposomal MTP-PE, they acquire the capacity to recognize and destroy neoplastic cells. Liposome-encapsulated MTP-PE has been shown to have antitumor effects in different types of cancer in dogs and cats, such as canine splenic angiosarcoma and melanoma, as well as feline and canine mammary adenocarcinoma (Fox et al., 1995; Vail et al., 1995; Teske et al., 1998; MacEwen et al., 1999).

An important drawback of the use of liposomes in vaccine formulations for productive animals is the high cost of purified phospholipids. Thus, liposomal preparations based on non-purified lipid extracts constitute an attractive tool for veterinary vaccinology. Following such approach, liposomes obtained from total egg yolk lipids were recently used to encapsulate an experimental DNA vaccine encoding Merozoite Surface Antigen-2c of the tick-transmitted hemoprotozoon *Babesia bovis* (Rodriguez et al., 2013). A dramatic increase in the number of mice that developed a humoral response against MSA-2c was observed in the group inoculated with liposome-encapsulated plasmid DNA, as compared to the group that received the naked plasmid. These experiments are indicative that liposomes made out of total egg yolk lipids may be applicable to a large variety of veterinary vaccines. Preparation of egg yolk liposomes is inexpensive, and the extract of one egg suffices for 300 DNA vaccine doses. Additionally, the procedure is fast, can be easily scaled-up and is likely suitable for the delivery of hydro or liposoluble therapeutic drugs as well.

3. Drug Delivery

Poor bioavailability and non-desired side effects limit the application of a great number of pharmacological agents in human and veterinary medicine. These problems can often be overcome by liposomes, as well as by other nanoparticles by: (i) allowing the delivery of water-insoluble agents, (ii) increasing the concentration of an agent at its desired location, and as a consequence, lowering systemic toxicity and drug concentration in healthy tissues, and (iii) reducing drug clearance, thus yielding sustained release during a prolonged period of time (Underwood & van Eps, 2012). Although applications in animals have been considerably less explored than in humans, there is sufficient evidence that liposomes can improve the delivery of several antimicrobials, anti-tumor and analgesic agents of veterinary use (Table 2). However, in spite of demonstration of their clear advantages, liposome applications have in most cases not surpassed the research boundaries.

Two decades ago, it has been described that liposome encapsulation considerably reduced the side effects of diamidine (imidocarb) in horses, while improving its efficacy in the treatment of equine piroplasmosis (Timofeev et al., 1994). However, non-encapsulated imidocarb continues being the drug of choice for this disease, and improved formulations with decreased toxicity are still pending (Kutscha et al., 2012).

Several research studies have analyzed the effects of liposomal drug formulations for the treatment of visceral leishmaniasis, an emergent disease in developing countries. The best known of such formulations is AmBisome, a liposomal preparation of amphotericin B, which inhibits ergosterol synthesis, and thus displays a potent antimycotic, as well as anti-leishmanial activity. Liposome encapsulation of amphotericin B improves the uptake of the drug by the reticuloendothelial system where *Leishmania* sp. parasites reside, and decreases its uptake by the kidney, thus significantly reducing its nephrotoxic effects (Meyerhoff, 1999). AmBisome was approved by the US Food and Drug Administration for the treatment of visceral leishmaniasis in humans and is commercially available (Meyerhoff, 1999). In dogs, the main reservoir of visceral leishmaniasis, experimental treatment with AmBisome was initially satisfactory but clinical signs reappeared after a few months (Oliva et al.,

2004). Additionally, since AmBisome is the main therapeutic drug for human leishmaniasis, its use in dogs is arguable due to the possible generation of drug-resistant parasites (Vulpiani et al., 2011).

Table 2. Liposome use in the delivery of drugs in the veterinary field

Drug activity	Drug	Disease	Target Species	Reference
Antimicrobial	Diamidine	Equine piroplasmosis	Horse	Timofeev et al., 1994
	Amphotericin B	Visceral leishmaniasis	Dog	Oliva et al., 2004
	Trifluralin			Marques et al., 2004; Carvalheiro et al., 2009
	Meglumine antimoniate			Ribeiro et al., 2008; da Silva et al., 2012
Antitumoral	Doxorubicin	Sarcoma	Cat, dog,	Teske et al., 2011, Kleiter et al., 2010
	Meta-tetra (hydroxyphenyl) chlorin	Squamous cell carcinoma	Cat	Buchholz et al., 2005
	Clodronate	Malignant histiocytosis	Dog	Hafeman et al., 2010
	Cisplatin	Osteosarcoma	Cat, dog	Thamm and Veil, 1998; Marr et al., 2004
Immunosuppresor	Clodronate	Spontaneous autoimmune hemolytic anemia	Dog	Mathes et al., 2006
Analgesic	Hydromorphone	Pain	Dog, Monkey	Krugner-Higby, 2011 a, b
	Butorphanol		Parrot	Paul-Murphy et al., 2009
Anti-inflammatory	Diclofenac	Inflammation	Horse	Lynn et al., 2004; Schleining et al., 2008; Levine et al., 2009; Frisbie et al., 2009.
Diagnostic imaging	Technetium-99m	Infection, inflammation, neoplasia	Cat, horse	Matteucci et al., 2000 ; Underwood et al., 2011 ;

Investigation of alternative therapeutic agents for canine leishmaniasis includes a few other liposomal formulations. Marques et al. (2008) studied the effects of i.v. injection of experimentally infected dogs with liposomal trifluralin, a dinitroaniline with proved *in vitro* anti-leishmanial activity. Liposomal trifluraline improved the clinical condition of the animals and reduced the parasite load. Accordingly, a protective anti-leishmanial response to liposomal trifluralin was obtained by Carvalheiro et al. (2009) in a mouse model. This study also showed that liposomal trifluralin was stable after freeze-drying, if trehalose was present in the surrounding medium, which can be of great significance for storage and distribution. Meglumine antimoniate was also formulated in liposomes and i.v. administered to dogs with visceral leishmaniasis, resulting in a significant decrease of parasite burden in lymph nodes, livers, and spleens, as well as a reduction in the rate of parasite transmission to sand flies fed on these animals. Importantly, these effects could be achieved with doses 20 times lower than those needed for the non-encapsulated drug, resulting in less-pronounced metal-induced side effects (Ribeiro et al., 2008). Interestingly, a combination of liposomal meglumine antimoniate and allopurinol resulted in complete clearance of the parasite from the liver, although the parasite could still be found in small amounts in the lymph nodes (da Silva et al., 2012).

The above presented studies show that liposomes can significantly improve the delivery and safety of different anti-leishmanial drugs in dogs. However, none of the formulations tested so far yielded a complete clearance of the parasite. Furthermore, it has to be taken into account that treatment of dogs with expensive liposomal formulations is not viable in developing countries. Because of veterinary and public health reasons, further search for effective and affordable therapeutic agents against canine leishmaniasis is needed (Vulpiani et al., 2011).

Liposomes have been widely applied to the encapsulation of anti-tumor agents to improve their targeted delivery and lower their toxic side effects. An example is provided by liposome-encapsulated cisplatin, which is commercially available under the name of Lipoplatin. Lipoplatin liposomes are composed of PC, cholesterol, dipalmitoylphosphatidylglycerol, and methoxy-polyethylene glycol-distearoyl PE. Polyethylene glycol (PEG), an inert substance, accumulates on the surface of these liposomes, rendering them undetectable by macrophages and immune cells. PEG-liposomes, also known as "stealth liposomes", have an extended circulation lifetime, which is a prerequisite for their extravasation and infiltration of tumors using imperfections in their vascular endothelium. Liposomes are avidly taken up by tumor cells, leading to a dramatic accumulation of the drug in cancerous as compared to adjacent healthy tissues. Importantly, Lipoplatin displays lower nephrotoxicity than non encapsulated cisplatin in humans (Boulikas, 2009).

In addition to its use in human medicine, cisplatin is recommended for the treatment of osteosarcoma in small animals, although due to its nephrotoxicity, hydration protocols need to accompany the treatment (Dernell et al., 2001). Lipoplatin, on the other hand, could be administered to healthy dogs in twice as high doses as the maximum allowed for the free drug, without the need of saline infusion (Marr et al., 2004). These studies agree well with those of Thamm and Veil (1998), who observed that antitumoral doses of cisplatin could be safely administered to healthy cats only when the drug was encapsulated in liposomes. Thus, Lipoplatin appears as a valid option for the treatment of cancer in cats and dogs.

Stealth liposomes have also been applied for the delivery of doxorubicin to cats and dogs in the treatment of soft tissue sarcomas and splenic hemangiosarcoma, respectively (Kleiter et al., 2010; Teske et al., 2011). Although liposomal doxorubicin has been reported to have a lower cytotoxicity in rabbits and dogs than the free drug (Working et al., 1999), this difference was not observed in the latter study. Interestingly, liposomes labeled with the radioisotope Technetium 99 were used to show that hyperthermia increases liposome accumulation in cat sarcomas indicating that controlled heat exposure increases the effectivity of liposomal anti-tumor drugs such as cisplatin or doxorubicin (Matteucci et al., 2000).

The photosensitizer meta-(tetrahydroxyphenyl) chlorin was also formulated in stealth liposomes and i.v. administered to cats with squamous cell carcinoma, followed by photodynamic therapy, which is intended to destroy tumor cells. The results showed that this liposomal formulation was safe, with no noticeable side effects, and showed higher selectivity and a significantly earlier tumor peak than the free drug, suggesting that it can provide an efficient and effective tool for photodynamic therapy (Buchholz et al., 2005).

On the other hand, non-pegylated liposomes are rapidly phagocytosed by macrophages. This characteristic was exploited for the selective killing of these cells by clodronate, an apoptosis-inducing bisphosphonate drug, to treat autoimmune hemolytic anemia and malignant histiocytosis in dogs (Mathes et al., 2006; Hafeman et al., 2010).

Administration of liposome-encapsulated opioids, such butorphanol and hydromorphone, ensures longer term analgesic activity with lower toxicity as compared to the non-encapsulated drug. The use of this kind of formulations for pain suppression has been successfully tested in dogs, monkeys, and parrots (Paul-Murphy et al., 2009; Krugner-Higby, 2011a,b). Also, a liposome-based diclofenac sodium cream was developed for transdermal use in horses. This formulation ensures ease of application, diffuses readily through skin into subcutaneous tissues, minimizes adverse systemic reactions as compared to parenteral administration of the drug and, most importantly, reduces horse limb inflammation due to several causes, such as synovitis and ostheoarthritis (Lynn et al., 2004; Schleining et al., 2008; Frisbie et al., 2009; Levine et al., 2009).

Lastly, radiolabeled PEG-liposomes can be used for diagnostic purposes, since they can extravasate at sites of increased vascular permeability and accumulate at sites of infection, ischemia, inflammation and neoplasia, which can be detected by scintigraphic imaging. Intravenous injection of Technectium 99m-labeled PEG-liposomes in healthy horses was well tolerated and resulted in a reproducible biodistribution pattern, which indicates that this approach can be useful for diagnostic imaging (Underwood et al., 2011). Additionally, this study showed a high accumulation of liposomes in the lung, which might be advantageous for the delivery of drugs targeting this tissue.

4. TRANSFECTION

In addition to their use in vaccination, nucleic acids can be incorporated into cells with the aim of therapies based on gene replacement or interference RNA, as well as for the production of transgenic organisms. Liposomes are one of the methods applied in these technologies to improve nucleic acid delivery to target cells (Niu & Liang, 2008). As an example, Yang et al. (2012) used liposomes to deliver small interfering RNA molecules (sRNA) encoding relevant antigens of the rabies virus (RABV), an on-going public health threat with so far no established curative therapy. They observed RABV-infected mice that received liposome entrapped sRNA showed significantly higher survival rates than mice that received the same sRNA without liposomes, indicating that this approach could provide a suitable prophylactic means against rabies.

Development and production of transgenic animals is widely used in research and is being increasingly applied in the veterinary field. Transfection of germ cells appears more efficient and cost-effective than transfection of embryos for transgenesis in mammals. Foreign DNA can be introduced in spermatozoa or oocytes by incubation or microinjection, and these procedures are greatly facilitated by liposome entrapment of the nucleic acid (Niu & Liang, 2008). In support of this view, incubation of rabbit sperm with liposome-DNA complexes, followed by *in vitro* fertilization led to the production of transgenic offspring expressing a gene of interest (Wang et al., 2003). Likewise, Vichera et al. (2011, 2012) injected liposomes and DNA encoding enhanced green fluorescent protein (EGFP) into pre-fertilized bovine oocytes and presumptive zygotes. A high percentage of the resulting embryos expressed EGFP, demonstrating a successful transfection.

5. Cryopreservation

Successful cryopreservation of semen was first achieved in the early XX century and is currently a regular practice in the breeding of productive and companion animals. Extended storage and shipment possibilities favor the use of cryopreserved over fresh semen for artificial insemination (Mara et al., 2013). Moreover, sperm cryopreservation is considered an effective strategy for the conservation of endangered animal species (Mazur et al., 2008). However, freezing and thawing can have dramatic effects on the viability and subsequent fertility of spermatozoa and the choice of adequate freezing extenders is crucial (Ricker et al., 2006). Egg yolk has long been employed as extender to cryopreserve semen of different animal species (Mara et al., 2013), but since its use is not practical and bears the risk of bacterial contamination, research has been focused on its replacement by defined, pathogen-free components. As it was reported that the phospholipid fraction of egg yolk is responsible for the protective effects on sperm during cooling (Quinn et al., 1980), it was hypothesized that liposomes constitute a useful freezing extender. Indeed, Röpke et al. (2011) showed that liposomes made of egg yolk PC (EPC) significantly increased pre-thaw viability of bovine spermatozoa incubated at 4 °C for up to one day, as well as their post-thaw survival. Interestingly, survival rates were higher if dioleoyl phosphatidylglycerol was included in the EPC liposome preparation in a 9:1 ratio, while this effect was not obtained with dioleoyl PS or dioleoyl PE. When liposomes were made out of PC containing saturated fatty acids, the results dramatically depended on the fatty acid chain length. Thus, liposomes of dilauroyl-PC (12 carbon atom-long fatty acids) were toxic and caused a complete loss in sperm viability, dimyristoyl-PC (14 carbon atoms) liposomes gave similar protection as those made of EPC, and dipalmitoyl-PC or distearoyl-PC liposomes (16 and 18 carbon atoms, respectively) were neither effective nor toxic (Röpke et al, 2011).

In a similar approach, Pillet et al. (2012) explored the applicability of liposomes made out of mixtures of egg yolk or soy bean phospholipids as a replacement of egg yolk in the cryopreservation of stallion semen. They found that supplementing a commercial extender with 4% liposomes (v/v) composed of commercial E80 lecithin (which contains mainly PC and smaller amounts of PE, sphingosine, lysoPC and lysoPE), encapsulating Hank´s salt-glucose lactose solution, yielded similar results as egg yolk, with respect to post-thaw sperm motility and membrane integrity. Moreover, fertility rates in mares inseminated with egg yolk- or liposome-exposed sperm were not significantly different.

These reports demonstrate that liposomes constitute a promising useful tool for cryopreservation of semen. Importantly, their composition appears to be a critical aspect to achieve the desired effects. It has been suggested that liposomes could serve as a source of phospholipids to replace lost molecules during the cooling procedure. However, Ricker et al. (2006) showed that exogenous lipids do not incorporate into the spermatozoa membrane, but instead, strongly associate with its surface providing a physical barrier to freeze-thaw damage and preventing membrane phase separation during cooling.

Although not specifically prepared as liposomes, extender supplementation with soy bean lecithin suspensions (5-10% v/v) proved useful to preserve post-thaw quality parameters and fertility of fish sperm, yielding similar results as egg yolk (Yildiz et al., 2013). This type of experiments suggests that liposomes are likely useful for the cryopreservation of gametes of a large variety of species.

Finally, in addition to their specific use as extender components, liposomes have provided a resourceful tool as models to analyze the effects of potential cryoprotectors on membrane stability of stallion sperm (Oldenhof et al., 2013).

CONCLUDING REMARKS

The above presented information shows that liposomes constitute an attractive component of the nanotechnology toolbox in the veterinary field, though an important gap exists between interesting research developments and the availability of marketable products. As compared to other nanotechnologies, poor stability might be the main drawback of liposome use, while advantages include lack of toxicity, versatility and easiness of preparation. On the other hand, production costs are significant when purified or synthetic lipids are employed. This might not be a limitation in therapeutic interventions of companion animals in industrialized countries or in transgenic technologies, yet will be a severe constraint for other liposome uses, such as massive vaccination of poultry, fish or cattle, or drug treatments of companion animals in developing countries. Thus, the use of inexpensive phospholipid sources for liposome production whenever possible might greatly potentiate the effective application of liposomes in animal health and husbandry.

ACKNOWLEDGMENTS

Financing by the European Commission (INCO 245145, PIROVAC) and MINCyT, Argentina (PICT 2010-430) is gratefully acknowledged. MFC, MLT and LS are researchers from the National Research Council of Argentina (CONICET), and AER is a researcher from the National Agricultural Technology Institute of Argentina (INTA).

REFERENCES

Bangham, A. D. & Horne, R.W. (1964) Negative staining of phospholipids and their structural modification by surface active agents as observed in the electron microscope. *J. Mol. Biol.,* 8, 660–8.

Boulikas, T. (2009) Clinical overview on Lipoplatin: a successful liposomal formulation of cisplatin. *Expert Opin. Investig. Drugs*, 18, 1197-218.

Buchholz, J., Kaser-Hotz, B., Khan, T., Rohrer Bley, C., Melzer, K., Schwendener, R.A., Roos, M. & Walt, H. (2005) Optimizing photodynamic therapy: *in vivo* pharmacokinetics of liposomal meta-(tetrahydroxyphenyl)chlorin in feline squamous cell carcinoma. *Clin. Cancer Res.,* 11, 7538-44.

Carvalheiro, M., Jorge, J., Eleuterio, C., Pinhal, A.F., Sousa, A.C., Morais, J.G. & Cruz, M.E. (2009) Trifluralin liposomal formulations active against *Leishmania donovani* infections. *Eur. J. Pharm. Biopharm.,* 71, 292-6.

da Silva, S. M., Amorim, I.F., Ribeiro, R.R., Azevedo, E.G., Demicheli, C., Melo, M.N., Tafuri, W.L., Gontijo, N.F., Michalick, M.S. & Frezard, F. (2012) Efficacy of combined therapy with liposome-encapsulated meglumine antimoniate and allopurinol in treatment of canine visceral leishmaniasis. *Antimicrob. Agents Chemother.,* 56, 2858-67.

Deamer, D.W. (2010) From “Banghasomes” to liposomes: A memoir of Alec Bangham, 1921–2010. *FASEB J.,* 24, 1308-10.

Dernell, W.S., Straw, R.C. & Withrow, S.J. (2001) Tumors of the skeletal system. In: Withrow SJ, MacEwen EG, eds. *Small animal clinical oncology*. 3rd ed. Philadelphia: WB Saunders Co, pp. 378–417.

Dissanayake, D.R., Wijewardana, T.G., Gunawardena, G.A. & Poxton, I.R. (2010) Potential use of a liposome-encapsulated mixture of lipopolysaccharide core types (R1, R2, R3 and R4) of Escherichia coli in controlling colisepticemia in chickens. *J. Med. Microbiol.*, 59, 100-7.

Donnelly, J.J., Wahren, B. & Liu, M.A (2005) DNA vaccines: progress and challenges. *J. Immunol.,* 175, 633-9.

Dow, S., Elmslie, R., Kurzman, I., MacEwen, G., Pericle, F. & Liggitt, D. (2005) Phase I study of liposome-DNA complexes encoding the interleukin-2 gene in dogs with osteosarcoma lung metastases. *Hum. Gene Ther.,* 16, 937–46.

Fan, Y., Wang, D., Hu, Y., Liu, J., Han, G., Zhao, X., Yuan, J., Liu, C., Liu, X. & Ni, X. (2012) Liposome and epimedium polysaccharide-propolis flavone can synergistically enhance immune effect of vaccine. *Int. J. Biol. Macromol.*, 50, 125-30.

Faurez, F., Dory, D., Le Moigne, V., Gravier, R. & Jestin, A. (2010) Biosafety of DNA vaccines: New generation of DNA vectors and current knowledge on the fate of plasmids after injection. *Vaccine,* 28, 3888–95.

Fox, L. E., MacEwen, E.G., Kurzman, I.D., Dubielzig, R.R., Helfand, S.C., Vail, D.M., Kisseberth, W., London, C., Madewell, B.R. & Rodriguez, C.O., Jr. (1995) Liposome-encapsulated muramyl tripeptide phosphatidylethanolamine for the treatment of feline mammary adenocarcinoma--a multicenter randomized double-blind study. *Cancer Biother.,* 10, 125-30.

Frisbie, D.D., McIlwraith, C.W., Kawcak, C.E., Werpy, N.M. & Pearce, G.L. (2009) Evaluation of topically administered diclofenac liposomal cream for treatment of horses with experimentally induced osteoarthritis. *Am. J. Vet. Res.,* 70, 210-5.

Gao, H., Fan, Y., Wang, D., Hu, Y., Liu, J., Zhao, X., Guo, L., Zhao, X., Yuan, J. & Zhang, F. (2012). Optimization on preparation condition of epimedium polysaccharide liposome and evaluation of its adjuvant activity. *Int. J. Bio.l Macromol.*, 50, 207-13.

Gregoriadis, G. & Ryman, B.E. (1971) Liposomes as carriers of enzymes or drugs: a new approach to the treatment of storage diseases. *Biochem. J.*, 124, 58P.

Hafeman, S., London, C., Elmslie, R. & Dow, S. (2010) Evaluation of liposomal clodronate for treatment of malignant histiocytosis in dogs. *Cancer Immunol. Immunother.,* 59, 441-52.

Hiszczyńska-Sawicka, E., Akhtar, M., Kay, G.W,, Holec-Gasior, L., Bickerstaffe, R., Kur, J. & Stankiewicz, M. (2010) The immune responses of sheep after DNA immunization with *Toxoplasma gondii* MAG1 antigen-with and without co-expression of ovine interleukin 6. *Vet. Immunol. Immunopathol.*, 136, 324-9.

Hiszczyńska-Sawicka, E., Olędzka, G., Holec-Gąsior, L., Li, H., Xu, J.B., Sedcole, R., Kur, Bickerstaffe, R. & Stankiewicz, M. (2011). Evaluation of immune responses in sheep induced by DNA immunization with genes encoding GRA1, GRA4, GRA6 and GRA7 antigens of *Toxoplasma gondii*. *Vet. Parasitol.*, 177, 281-9.

Hiszczyńska-Sawicka, E., Li, H., Boyu Xu, J., Akhtar, M., Holec-Gasior, L., Kur, J., Bickerstaffe, R. & Stankiewicz, M. (2012). Induction of immune responses in sheep by vaccination with liposome-entrapped DNA complexes encoding *Toxoplasma gondii* MIC3 gene. *Pol. J. Vet. Sci.*, 15, 3-9.

Immordino, M.L., Dosio, F. & Cattel, L. (2006) Stealth liposomes: review of the basic science, rationale, and clinical applications, existing and potential. *Int. J. Nanomedicine.*, 1, 297-315.

Irie, T., Watarai, S., Iwasaki, T. & Kodama, H. (2005). Protection against experimental *Aeromonas salmonicida* infection in carp by oral immunisation with bacterial antigen entrapped liposomes. *Fish Shellfish Immunol.*, 18, 235-42.

Kleiter, M., Tichy, A., Willmann, M., Pagitz, M. & Wolfesberger, B. (2010) Concomitant liposomal doxorubicin and daily palliative radiotherapy in advanced feline soft tissue sarcomas. *Vet. Radiol. Ultrasound,* 51, 349-55.

Krugner-Higby, L., KuKanich, B., Schmidt, B., Heath, T.D. & Brown, C. (2011a) Pharmacokinetics and behavioral effects of liposomal hydromorphone suitable for perioperative use in rhesus macaques. *Psychopharmacology (Berl),* 216, 511-23.

Krugner-Higby, L., Smith, L., Schmidt, B., Wunsch, L., Smetana, A., Brown, C. & Heath, T.D. (2011b) Experimental pharmacodynamics and analgesic efficacy of liposome-encapsulated hydromorphone in dogs. *J. Am. Anim. Hosp. Assoc.,* 47, 185-95.

Kutscha, J., Sutton, D.G., Preston, T. & Guthrie, A.J. (2012) Equine piroplasmosis treatment protocols: specific effect on orocaecal transit time as measured by the lactose 13C-ureide breath test. *Equine Vet. J.*, 44 Suppl 43, 62-7.

Levine, D. G., Epstein, K.L., Neelis, D.A. & Ross, M.W. (2009) Effect of topical application of 1% diclofenac sodium liposomal cream on inflammation in healthy horses undergoing intravenous regional limb perfusion with amikacin sulfate. *Am. J. Vet. Res.,* 70, 1323-5.

Lewis, P.J. & Babiuk, L.A. (1999) DNA vaccines: a review. *Adv. Virus Res.*, 54, 129-88.

Li, W., Watarai, S., Iwasaki, T. & Kodama, H. (2004) Suppression of *Salmonella enterica* serovar Enteritidis excretion by intraocular vaccination with fimbriae proteins incorporated in liposomes. *Dev. Comp. Immunol.*, 28, 29-38.

Lynn, R.C., Hepler, D.I., Kelch, W.J., Bertone, J.J., Smith, B.L. & Vatistas, N.J. (2004) Double-blinded placebo-controlled clinical field trial to evaluate the safety and efficacy of topically applied 1% diclofenac liposomal cream for the relief of lameness in horses. *Vet. Ther.*, 5, 128-38.

MacEwen, E. G., Kurzman, I.D., Vail, D.M., Dubielzig, R.R., Everlith, K., Madewell, B.R., Rodriguez, C.O., Jr., Phillips, B., Zwahlen, C.H., Obradovich, J., Rosenthal, R.C., Fox, L.E., Rosenberg, M., Henry, C. & Fidel, J. (1999) Adjuvant therapy for melanoma in dogs: results of randomized clinical trials using surgery, liposome-encapsulated muramyl tripeptide, and granulocyte macrophage colony-stimulating factor. *Clin. Cancer Res.*, 5, 4249-58.

Mara, L., Casu, S., Carta, A. & Dattena, M. (2013) Cryobanking of farm animal gametes and embryos as a means of conserving livestock genetics. *Anim. Reprod. Sci.*, in press.

Marques, C., Carvalheiro, M., Pereira, M.A., Jorge, J., Cruz, M.E. & Santos-Gomes, G.M. (2008) Efficacy of the liposome trifluralin in the treatment of experimental canine leishmaniosis. *Vet. J.*, 178**,** 133-7.

Marr, A.K., Kurzman, I.D. & Vail, D.M. (2004) Preclinical evaluation of a liposome-encapsulated formulation of cisplatin in clinically normal dogs. *Am. J. Vet. Res.*, 65, 1474-8.

Mathes, M., Jordan, M. & Dow, S. (2006) Evaluation of liposomal clodronate in experimental spontaneous autoimmune hemolytic anemia in dogs. *Exp. Hematol.*, 34, 1393-402.

Matteucci, M. L., Anyarambhatla, G., Rosner, G., Azuma, C., Fisher, P.E., Dewhirst, M.W., Needham, D. & Thrall, D.E. (2000) Hyperthermia increases accumulation of technetium-99m-labeled liposomes in feline sarcomas. *Clin. Cancer Res.*, 6, 3748-55.

Mavichak, R., Takano, T., Kondo, H., Hirono, H., Wada, S., Hatai, K., Inagawa, H., Takahashi, Y., Yoshimura, T., Kiyono, H., Yuki, Y. & Aoki, T. (2010). The effect of liposome-coated recombinant protein VP28 against white spot syndrome virus in kuruma shrimp, Marsupenaeus japonicas. *Journal of Fish Diseases,* 33, 69–74

Mazur, P., Leibo, S.P. & Seidel, G.E., Jr. (2008) Cryopreservation of the germplasm of animals used in biological and medical research: importance, impact, status, and future directions. *Biol. Reprod.*, 78, 2–12.

Meyerhoff, A. (1999) U.S. Food and Drug Administration approval of AmBisome liposomal amphotericin B) for treatment of visceral leishmaniasis. *Clin. Infect. Dis.*, 28, 42–51

Mueller, R.S., Veir, J., Fieseler, K.V. & Dow, S.W. (2005) Use of immunostimulatory liposome-nucleic acid complexes in allergen-specific immunotherapy of dogs with refractory atopic dermatitis - a pilot study. *Vet. Dermatol.*, 16, 61-8.

Nishikawa, Y., Zhang, H., Ikehara, Y., Kojima, N., Xuan, X. & Yokoyama, N. (2009) Immunization with oligomannose-coated liposome-entrapped dense granule protein7 protects dams and offspring from *Neospora caninum* infection in mice. *Clin. Vaccine Immunol.*, 16, 792–7.

Nishimura, M., Kohara, J., Kuroda, Y., Hiasa, J., Tanaka, S., Muroi, Y., Kojima, N., Furuoka, H. & Nishikawa, Y. (2013). Oligomannose-coated liposome-entrapped dense granule protein 7 induces protective immune response to *Neospora caninum* in cattle. *Vaccine*, in press.

Niu, Y. & Liang, S. (2008) Progress in gene transfer by germ cells in mammals. *J. Genet. Genomics*, 35, 701-14.

Oldenhof, H., Gojowsky, M., Wang, S., Henke, S., Yu, C., Rohn, K., Wolkers, W.F. & Sieme, H. (2013) Osmotic stress and membrane phase changes during freezing of stallion sperm: mode of action of cryoprotective agents. *Biol. Reprod.*, 88, 68.

Oliva, G., Foglia Manzillo, V. & Pagano, A. (2004) Canine leishmaniasis: evolution of the chemotherapeutic protocols. *Parassitologia,* 46, 231-4.

Pang, Y., Wang, H., Li, Z., Piao, J., Piao, J., Chi, Y., Jin, J., Liu, Q. & Li, W. (2012) Immune response to liposome-associated recombinant SEF21 following oral immunization in chickens. *Avian Dis.*, 56, 347-53.

Parmentier, H. K., Klompen, A. L., De Vries Reilingh, G. & Lammers, A. (2008). Effect of concurrent intratracheal lipopolysaccharide and human serum albumin challenge on primary and secondary antibody responses in poultry. *Vaccine,* 26, 5510–20.

Paul-Murphy, J. R., Sladky, K.K., Krugner-Higby, L.A., Stading, B.R., Klauer, J.M., Keuler, N.S., Brown, C.S. & Heath, T.D. (2009) Analgesic effects of carprofen and liposome-encapsulated butorphanol tartrate in Hispaniolan parrots (*Amazona ventralis*) with experimentally induced arthritis. *Am. J. Vet. Res.,* 70, 1201-10.

Pillet, E., Labbe, C., Batellier, F., Duchamp, G., Beaumal, V., Anton, M., Desherces, S., Schmitt, E. & Magistrini, M. (2012) Liposomes as an alternative to egg yolk in stallion freezing extender. *Theriogenology* 77, 268-79.

Quinn, P.J., Chow, P.Y. & White, I.G. (1980) Evidence that phospholipid protects ram spermatozoa from cold shock at a plasma membrane site. *J. Reprod. Fertil.*, 60, 403–7.

Ribeiro, R. R., Moura, E.P., Pimentel, V.M., Sampaio, W.M., Silva, S.M., Schettini, D.A., Alves, C.F., Melo, F.A., Tafuri, W.L., Demicheli, C., Melo, M.N., Frezard, F. & Michalick, M.S. (2008) Reduced tissue parasitic load and infectivity to sand flies in dogs naturally infected by *Leishmania (Leishmania) chagasi* following treatment with a liposome formulation of meglumine antimoniate. *Antimicrob. Agents Chemother.*, 52, 2564-72.

Ricker, J.V., Linfor, J.J., Delfino, W.J., Kysar, P., Scholtz, E.L., Tablin, F., Crowe, J.H., Ball, B.A. & Meyers, S.A. (2006) Equine sperm membrane phase behavior: the effects of lipid-based cryoprotectants. *Biol. Reprod.*, 74, 359-65.

Rodriguez, A.E., Zamorano. P., Wilkowsky, S., Torrá, F., Ferreri, L., Dominguez, M. & Florin-Christensen, M. (2013) Delivery of recombinant vaccines against bovine herpesvirus type 1 gD and *Babesia bovis* MSA-2c to mice using liposomes derived from egg yolk lipids. *Vet. J.*, 196, 550-1.

Röpke, T., Oldenhof, H., Leiding, C., Sieme, H., Bollwein, H. & Wolkers, W.F. (2011) Liposomes for cryopreservation of bovine sperm. *Theriogenology*, 76, 1465–72

Schleining, J. A., McClure, S.R., Evans, R.B., Hyde, W.G., Wulf, L.W. & Kind, A.J. (2008) Liposome-based diclofenac for the treatment of inflammation in an acute synovitis model in horses. *J. Vet. Pharmacol. Ther.*, 31, 554-61.

Sessa, G. & Weissmann, G. (1968) Phospholipid spherules (liposomes) as a model for biological membranes. *J. Lipid Res.*, 9, 310–8.

Singha, H., Mallick, A.I., Jana, C., Fatima, N., Owais, M. & Chaudhuri, P. (2011) Co-immunization with interleukin-18 enhances the protective efficacy of liposomes encapsulated recombinant Cu-Zn superoxide dismutase protein against *Brucella abortus. Vaccine,* 29, 4720-7.

Sun, K., Li, X., Jiang, J., Cheng, A., Wang, M., Zhu, D., Jia, R., Chen, S., Zhou, Y., Chen, X. & Wang, X. (2013) Distribution characteristics of DNA vaccine encoded with glycoprotein C from Anatid herpesvirus 1 with chitosan and liposome as deliver carrier in ducks. *Virology J.,* 10, 89.

Takagi, H., Furuya, N. & Kojima, N. (2007) Preferential production of IL-12 by peritoneal macrophages activated by liposomes prepared from neoglycolipids containing oligomannose residues. *Cytokine,* 40, 241–50.

Teske, E., Rutteman, G.R., vd Ingh, T.S., van Noort, R. & Misdorp, W. (1998) Liposome-encapsulated muramyl tripeptide phosphatidylethanolamine (L-MTP-PE): a randomized clinical trial in dogs with mammary carcinoma. *Anticancer Res.,* 18, 1015-9.

Teske, E., Rutteman, G.R., Kirpenstein, J. & Hirschberger, J. (2011) A randomized controlled study into the efficacy and toxicity of pegylated liposome encapsulated doxorubicin as an adjuvant therapy in dogs with splenic haemangiosarcoma. *Vet. Comp. Oncol.,* 9, 283-9.

Thakur, A., Aagaard, C., Stockmarr, A., Andersen, P. & Jungersen, G. (2013) Cell-mediated and humoral immune responses after immunization of calves with a recombinant multiantigenic *Mycobacterium avium* subsp. paratuberculosis subunit vaccine at different ages. *Clin. Vaccine Immunol.*, 20, 551-8.

Thamm, D.H. & Vail, D.M. (1998) Preclinical evaluation of a sterically stabilized liposome-encapsulated cisplatin in clinically normal cats. *Am. J. Vet. Res.*, 59, 286-9.

Timofeev, B.A., Bolotin, I.M., Stepanova, L.P., Bogdanov, A.A. Jr., Georgiu, K., Malyshev, S. N., Petrovsky, V.V., Klibanov, A.L. & Torchilin, V.P. (1994) Liposomal diamidine (imidocarb): preparation and animal studies. *J. Microencapsul.,* 11, 627-32.

Torchilin, V.P. (2005) Recent advances with liposomes as pharmaceutical carriers. *Nat. Rev. Drug Discov.,* 4, 145-60.

U'Ren, L.W., Biller, B.J., Elmslie, R.E., Thamm, D.H. & Dow, S.W. (2007). Evaluation of a Novel Tumor Vaccine in Dogs with Hemangiosarcoma. *J. Vet. Intern. Med.*, 21, 113–20.

Underwood, C., van Eps, A.W., Ross, M.W., Laverman, P., van Bloois, L., Storm, G. & Schaer, T.P. (2011) Intravenous technetium-99m labelled PEG-liposomes in horses: a safety and biodistribution study. *Equine Vet. J.,* 44, 196-202.

Underwood, C. & van Eps, A.W. (2012) Nanomedicine and veterinary science: The reality and the practicality. *Vet. J.,* 193, 12-23.

Usui, T., Konnai, S., Tajima, S., Watarai, S., Aida, Y., Ohashi, K. & Onuma, M. (2003) Protective effects of vaccination with bovine leukemia virus (BLV) Tax DNA against BLV infection in sheep. *J. Vet. Med. Sci.*, 65, 1201-5.

Vail, D.M., MacEwen, E.G., Kurzman, I.D., Dubielzig, R.R., Helfand, S.C., Kisseberth, W.C., London, C.A., Obradovich, J.E., Madewell, B.R., Rodriguez, C.O., Jr. & et al. (1995) Liposome-encapsulated muramyl tripeptide phosphatidylethanolamine adjuvant immunotherapy for splenic hemangiosarcoma in the dog: a randomized multi-institutional clinical trial. *Clin. Cancer Res.,* 1, 1165-70.

Veir, J.K., Lappin, M.R. & Dow, S.W. (2006). Evaluation of a novel immunotherapy for treatment of chronic rhinitis in cats. *J. Feline Med. Surg.*, 8, 400-11.

Vichera, G., Moro, L.N. & Salamone, D. (2011) Efficient transgene expression in IVF and parthenogenetic bovine embryos by intracytoplasmic injection of DNA-liposome complexes. *Reprod. Domest. Anim.*, 46, 214-20.

Vichera, G., Moro, L.N., Buemo, C. & Salamone, D. (2012) DNA fragmentation, transgene expression and embryo development after intracytoplasmic injection of DNA-liposome complexes in IVF bovine zygotes. *Zygote*, 1, 1-9.

Vulpiani, M.P., Iannetti, L., Paganico, D., Iannino, F. & Ferri, N. (2011) Methods of control of the *Leishmania infantum* dog reservoir: state of the art. *Vet. Med. Internatl.*, 2011, 215964.

Wang, H.J., Lin, A.X. & Chen, Y.F. (2003) Association of rabbit sperm cells with exogenous DNA. *Anim. Biotechnol.*, 14, 155-65.

Working, P.K., Newman, M.S., Sullivan, T. & Yarrington, J. (1999) Reduction of the cardiotoxicity of doxorubicin in rabbits and dogs by encapsulation in long-circulating, pegylated liposomes. *J. Pharmacol. Exp. Ther.*, 289, 1128-33.

Yang, Y.J., Zhao, P.S., Zhang, T., Wang, H.L., Liang, H.R., Zhao, L.L., Wu, H.X., Wang, T.C., Yang, S.T., Xia, X.Z. (2012) Small interfering RNAs targeting the rabies virus nucleoprotein gene. *Virus Res.*, 169, 169-74.

Yaguchi, K., Ohgitani, T., Noro, T., Kaneshige, T. & Shimizu, Y. (2009) Vaccination of chickens with liposomal inactivated avian pathogenic *Escherichia coli* (APEC) vaccine by eye drop or coarse spray administration. *Avian Dis.*, 53, 245-9.

Yildiz, C., Bozkurt, Y. & Yavas, I. (2013) An evaluation of soybean lecithin as an alternative to avian egg yolk in the cryopreservation of fish sperm. *Cryobiology*, 67, 91-94.

Yu, Y., Wang, D., Abula, S., Hu, Y., Zhao, X., Huang, Y., Liu, J., Wu, Y., Wang, D., Tao, Y. & Pan, H. (2013) The immunological adjuvant activity of gypenosides liposome against Newcastle disease vaccine. *Int. J. Biol. Macromol.*, 60, 116-121.

Yuan, J., Liu, J., Hu, Y., Fan, Y., Wang, D., Guo, L., Nguyen, T.L., Zhao, X., Liu, X., Liu, C. & Wu, Y. (2012) The immunological activity of propolis flavonoids liposome on the immune response against ND vaccine. *Int. J. Biol. Macromol.*, 51, 400-5.

Yuan, J., Lu, Y., Abula, S., Hu, Y., Liu, J., Fan, Y., Zhao, X., Wang, D., Liu, X.& Liu, C. (2013) Optimization on preparation condition of propolis flavonoids liposome by response surface methodology and research of its immunoenhancement activity. *Evid. Based Complement Alternat. Med.*, 2013, 505703.

Zhang, H., Nishikawa, Y., Yamagishi, J., Zhou, J., Ikehara, Y., Kojima, N., Yokoyama, N. & Xuan, X. (2010) *Neospora caninum*: application of apical membrane antigen 1 encapsulated in the oligomannose-coated liposomes for reduction of offspring mortality from infection in BALB/c mice. *Exp. Parasitol.*, 125, 130-6.

Zhao, X., Fan, Y., Wang, D., Hu, Y., Guo, L., Ruan, S., Zhang, J. & Yuan, J. (2011) Immunological adjuvant efficacy of glycyrrhetinic acid liposome against Newcastle disease vaccine. *Vaccine*, 29, 9611-7.

Zinsstag, J., Schelling, E., Waltner-Toews, D. & Tanner, M. (2011) From "one medicine" to "one health" and systemic approaches to health and well-being. *Prev. Vet. Med.*, 101, 148-156.

In: Advances in Liposomes Research
Editor: Lauren Finney
ISBN: 978-1-63117-074-4

Chapter 6

DESIGN OF LIPOSOMES WITH A pH-SENSITIVE FLUORESCENT DYE AND GRAMICIDIN CHANNELS FOR IMMUNE-SENSING

Atsushi Shoji[1,2]·Misato Sakamoto[1]· and Masao Sugawara*[1]

[1]Department of Chemistry, College of Humanities and Sciences, Nihon University, Sakurajousui, Setagaya, Tokyo, Japan

[2]Division of Pharmaceutical and Biomedical Analysis, School of Pharmacy, Tokyo University of Pharmacy and Life Science, Hachioji-shi, Tokyo, Japan

ABSTRACT

In this review, we describe a liposome array for direct fluorometric immunoassay using liposomes encapsulating a pH-sensitive fluorescent dye, BCECF ([2',7'-bis(carboxyethyl)-4 or 5-carboxyfluorescein]). The method has a signal amplification system based on modulation of channel kinetics of gramicidin, which forms a nanopore in a lipid bilayer and allows permeating monovalent cations. The detection of analytes is performed without any lysis of liposomes and labeling with a fluorescent

*Department of Chemistry, College of Humanities and Sciences, Nihon University, Sakurajousui, Setagaya, Tokyo 156-8550, Japan, e-mail: sugawara@chs.nihon-u.ac.jp.

molecule. Instead, immunoreactions between analyte and $F_{ab'}$ fragment linked to liposomes are monitored though a fluorescence change of the encapsulated dye, which depends on the channel activity of gramicidin. The assay is simple, rapid and highly sensitive. The method allowed quantification of substance P (SP), neurokinin A, growth-hormone-related peptides, and streptolysin O (SLO) at sub-pg to ng level. The highly sensitive assay was applied to detection of SP and SLO in human serum by simply diluting the sample 125 times (0.8% human serum). The method has the potential of applying it as a bioanalytical technique for clinical analyses and diagnoses.

INTRODUCTION

Liposomes, which were discovered by Bangham et al. [1], have been widely utilized as an analytical tool for detecting biomolecules owing to its high surface area, large internal volume and ability to conjugate bilayer lipids with a variety of antibodies. The quantification of biomolecules in liposome-based immuno-sensing is commonly achieved by either a competitive or a sandwich format. Liposomes can encapsulate a variety of signal markers, such as dye [2-14], enzyme [14-21], electrochemical [22-25] and chemiluminescent markers [26-28]. Consequently, liposome-based immuno-sensing has the advantage that an analytical signal is an amplified one based on the principle of signal transduction [29-31].

In liposome-based immuno-sensing, the detection of intact liposomes encapsulating a dye is one of the successful strategies of signal amplification (Fig. 1a). There are a number of studies on the strip-based liposome immunoassay, which utilizes an antibody-immobilized plastic nitorocellulose strip [2-9]. For signal amplification, sulforhodamine B is usually used as an encapsulated dye in liposomes. The assay is one of common and efficient analytical techniques for point of care diagnosis due to simple and low cost instrument. On the other hand, liposome lysis immunoassays (Fig. 1b) are another strategy for signal amplification, which is relied on detecting a signal marker released from liposomes by lysis. In this assay, detection limit for an analyte is significantly lower as compared with liposome immunoassay based on detecting intact liposomes. The lysis of liposomes is achieved by using reagents such as surfactant [11, 13, 17, 22-25], enzyme (phospholipase C (PLC) and trypsin) [32, 33] and complement [10, 12, 34]. Similar to the strip-based liposome immunoassay, fluorescence dyes is used as a signal marker. In this case, fluorescence enhancement is achieved through release of entrapped self-quenching dyes, such as calcein [35, 36], fluoresceine [37], carboxyfluorescein [10], sulforhodamine 101 [38] and sulforhodamine B [11-14]. Further, one can extend signal markers to electrochemical reagents [22, 23, 24], enzyme [21] and its substrate [24]. The liposome lysis immunoassay is often combined with flow-injection analysis [39-40], providing high sensitivity, short testing period, recycling, and the use of an automated instrument.

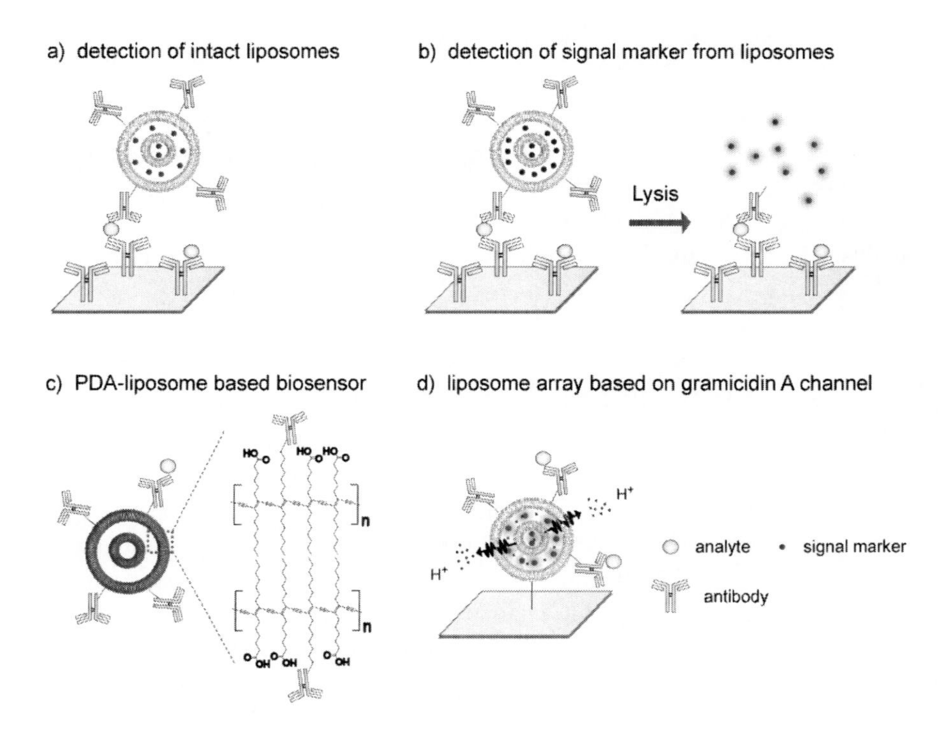

Figure 1. Schematic illustration for liposome-based immunoassays. a) Detection of intact liposomes. b) Detection of signal marker from liposomes. c) PDA-liposome based biosensor. d) A liposome array based on gramicidin A channel.

In contrast to above-mentioned indirect assays, very few studies have been reported on direct assays, which measure changes in the physical and chemical properties of lipid bilayers caused by antigen-antibody immuno reaction. For example, polydiacetylene (PDA) has been employed in direct liposome immunoassay, taking the advantage that color of PDA changes in response to heating, solvent change and pH [41] (Fig. 1c). A PDA liposome-based biosensor has been applied for quantification of E. coli [42], streptavidin [43] and hepatotoxin microcystin-LR [44]. This assay as well has the advantage that labeling of analyte and separation steps are not necessary. Our approach for direct immunoassay (Fig. 1d) is based on modulation of monomer/dimmer formation kinetics of a gramicidin channel in a lipid bilayer [45-47]. In this system, a large number of H^+ ions are released through gramicidin channels formed in a lipid bilayer, which is detected as a change in the fluorescence intensity of an encapsulated pH-sensitive dye BCECF ([2',7'-bis(carboxyethyl)-4 or 5-carboxyfluorescein]). In this review, we describe highly sensitive immunoassays with a liposome array based on modulation of monomer/dimmer channel kinetics of gramicidin and their application to determination of some biomolecules in biological fluids.

Liposome immunoassay in an array format is highly sensitive and has the advantage that labeling of analyte and B/F separation steps are not necessary. The array has the potential of designing a comprehensive and simultaneous analysis system, similar to protein [48], peptide [49], DNA and RNA chips [50, 51].

PRINCIPLE OF DIRECT IMMUNOASSAY WITH A LIPOSOME ARRAY

The principle of signal amplification based on the modulation of channel kinetics of gramicidin is shown in Fig. 2. Since antibody is conjugated to liposome surface, the membrane bound antibody (receptor) is apparently independent from gramicidin channels. However, immunoreaction at the liposome surface modulates the dimer/monomer formation kinetics of gramicidin, because of a local stress of the bilayer induced by the immunoreaction. This feature allows us to measure directly a change in fluorescence emitted from liposomes in an array format. For preparing an array, a Fab' fragment of antibody for an analyte is conjugated on the surface of liposomes. The immune-liposomes encapsulating a pH-sensitive fluorescent dye BCECF ([2',7'-bis(carboxyethyl)-4 or 5-carboxyfluorescein]) is spotted on a surface-activated glass slip. The spotted liposomes have an inner solution of pH5.5 and contain BCECF. At pH 5.5, BCECF is weakly fluorescent. For assay, the spot is incubated with an analyte in an outer solution (pH 7.8), and then gramicidin is added to the outer solution. When a gramicidin channel is formed in the lipid bilayer, release of H^+ ions occurs through the gramicidin channel, leading to a rise in pH of the inner solution. Consequently, acid dissociation of the dye proceeds in the inner solution, forming a strongly fluorescent BCECF anion. Since a lipid bilayer is not permeable to the BCECF anions, fluorescence emission is observed from the liposomes. Although gramicidin is not directly linked to receptor sites, the activity of gramicidin is modulated by an immunoreaction at the bilayer surface, owing to a local distortion of the bilayer structure. The distortion is related to antigen binding. The larger is the amount of bound antigen, the larger is the distortion of the bilayers, and hence fluorescence emission from the BCECF encapsulating-liposomes is antigen concentration-dependent.

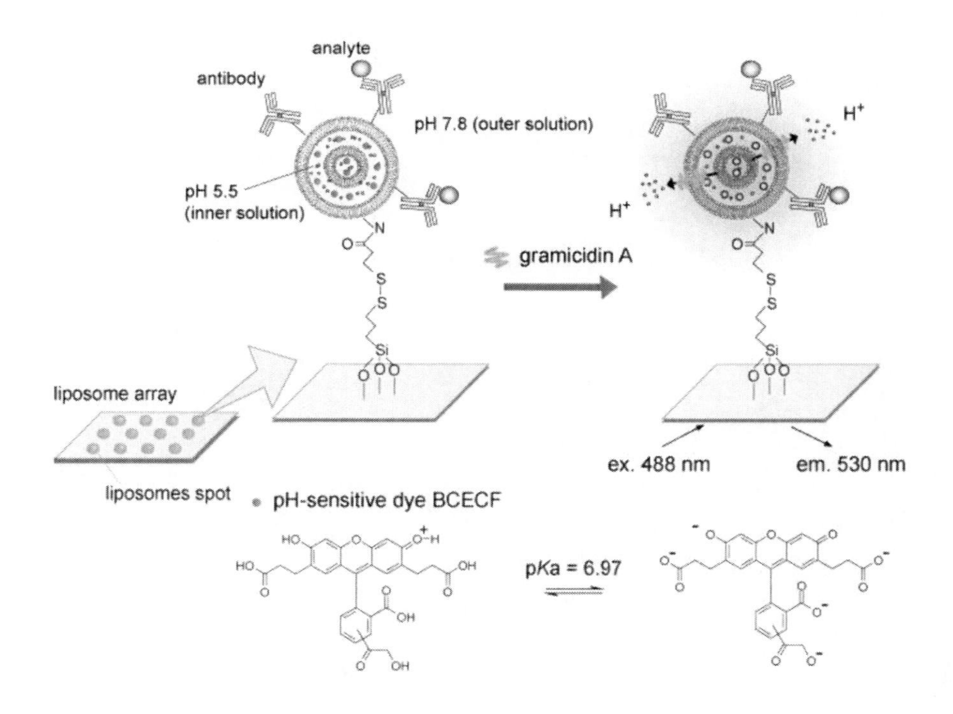

Figure 2. Schematic illustration of principle of a gramicidin-aided liposome array.

A Reusable Liposome Array

There are different methods for immobilization of liposomes on substrates, such as covalent binding [52-54], biotin-avidin interaction [45,55,56], electrostatic interaction [57,58], DNA hybridization [59, 60].

Covalent binding is the most robust and widely used for immobilizing liposomes on various substrates. Many researchers have used amine coupling techniques using *N*-hydroxysuccinimide (NHS). In this technique, carboxyl groups on a substrate and an amino head group of lipid is coupled each other [54]. The immobilization of liposomes using an interaction between avidin and biotin has also been reported [45]. However, these robust bonds are not easy to cleave them.

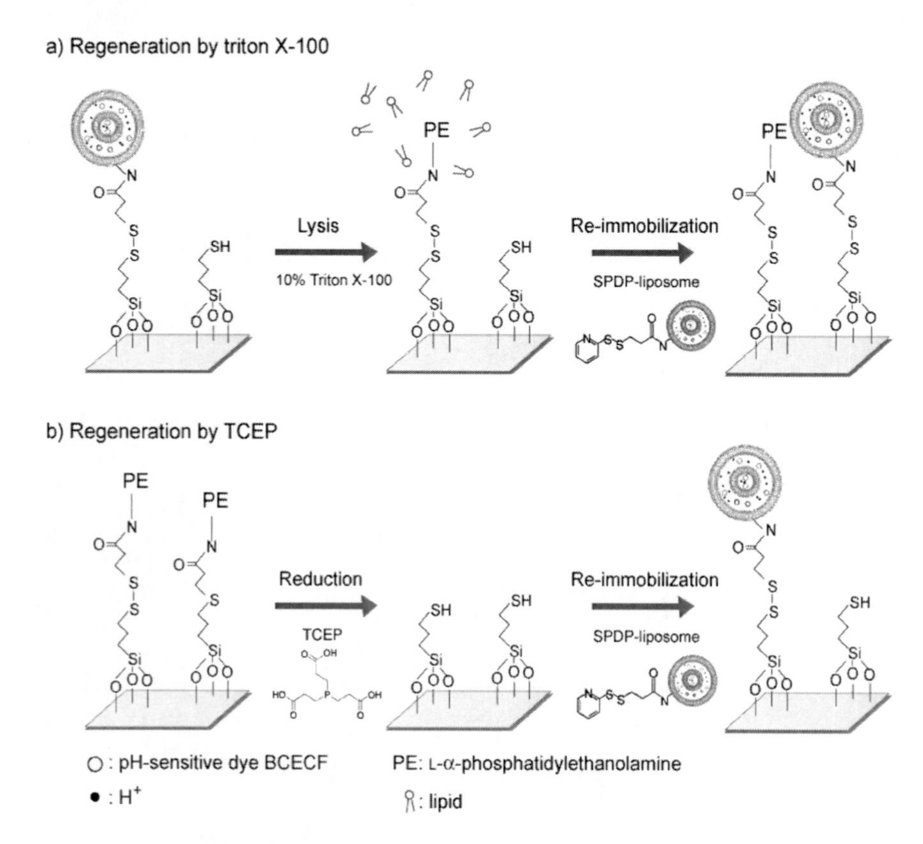

Figure 3. Schematic illustration for reuse of a liposome array.

To design a reusable liposome array, the cleavage of chemical bonds between liposomes and substrates are required. For this purpose, we investigated the immobilization of liposomes on glass slips utilizing the thiol coupling technique. The procedure for preparing a reusable liposome array and the working principle of reuse of the array is schematically shown in Fig. 3.

The one-side surface of a cover slip (76 × 26 mm) is treated with 0.40 mL of 50% v/v 3-mercaptopropyltrimethoxysilane (MTS) in toluene for 60 min at room temperature (designated as a MTS slip). After washing with toluene, the MTS slip is spotted with each 10-μl portion of a diluted suspension of the *N*-succinimidyl 3-(2-pyridyldithio)-propionate (SPDP)-modified liposomes encapsulating BCECF. The liposome spot is washed by adding a 10 mM 2-morpholinoethanesulfonic acid buffer solution (pH 7.8; abbreviated as a Mes solution) with a micropipette and aspirating the solution with Kimwipe paper. The spot is incubated with Fab' fragments, in order to couple the Fab' fragment to liposome surface. Thus prepared liposome array is used for immunoassay.

The liposome array is regenerated by treatment with a lysis agent triton X-100 and a reducing agent tris(2-carboxyethyl)phosphine hydrochloride (TCEP). The triton X-100 treatment causes lysis of liposome, though disulfide bonds which cross-link SPDP-liposomes onto the slip are uncleaved by this treatment. One way for reuse the slip is to use residual sulfhydryl sites on each spot for re-immobilization of SPDP-liposomes. However, when a liposome slip is repeatedly used and treated with triton X-100, the number of PE molecules remaining on the slip increases, thereby occupying most of sulfhydryl sites that are necessary for cross-linking reaction. Therefore, PE molecules on the slip are removed by cleaving disulfide bonds with a reducing agent TCEP.

GRAMICIDIN-AIDED FLUORESCENCE CHANGE OF LIPOSOMES

Gramicidin A allows permeation of monovalent cations through the formation of a transmembrane dimmer [61]. Since fluorescence enhancement in the gramicidin-aided assay is due to the translocation of H^+ ions through gramicidin channels, the number of gramicidin channels is a key factor for the response property. What we expect with respect to gramicidin concentration is that the larger is the concentration of gramicidin, the faster is the response time of the system. Comparison of the time required for fluorescence enhancement at different concentrations of gramicidin is shown in Fig. 4. At 1 μg/mL gramicidin, the fluorescence intensity became practically saturated beyond 10 min. As compared with the result (50 min) with 10 ng/mL gramicidin, the time required for fluorescence enhancement was significantly short. Furthermore, the observed fluorescence change (ΔF) is approximately 1.5 times larger than that obtained with 10 ng/mL gramicidin, seemingly because a pH rise of the inner solution is larger. On the basis of this feature, rapid immunoassay is attained.

Gramicidin channels are permeable to monovalent cations, such as H^+ and Na^+ [61], but monovalent metal ions, especially Na^+ ions in the present case, do not interfere with the method, simply because encapsulated BCECF is only sensitive to H^+ ions. It is noted that the gramicidin-induced fluorescent enhancement is observed only for the case that liposomes are immobilized on a cover slip, while only a small change is observed in the case that gramicidin is added to liposomes in a bulk solution (Fig. 5).

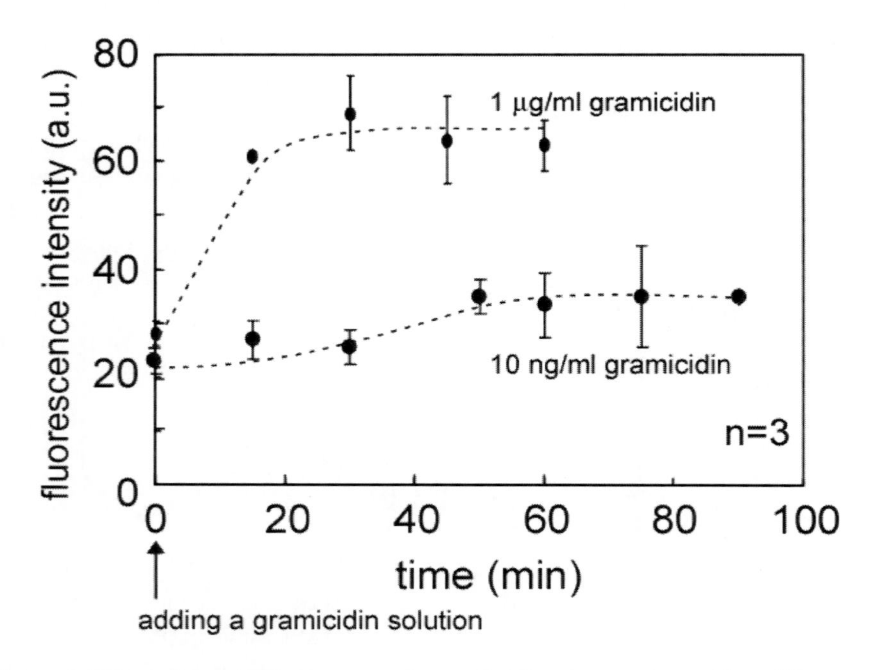

Figure 4. Effect of gramicidin concentration on the fluorescence intensities of B-cap-PE containing liposomes in the presence of avidin. Gramicidin concentrations: (a) 1.0 µg/mL and (b) 10 ng/mL. Ex.488 nm; Em. 530 nm. Error bars indicate means ± standard deviations (n = 3).

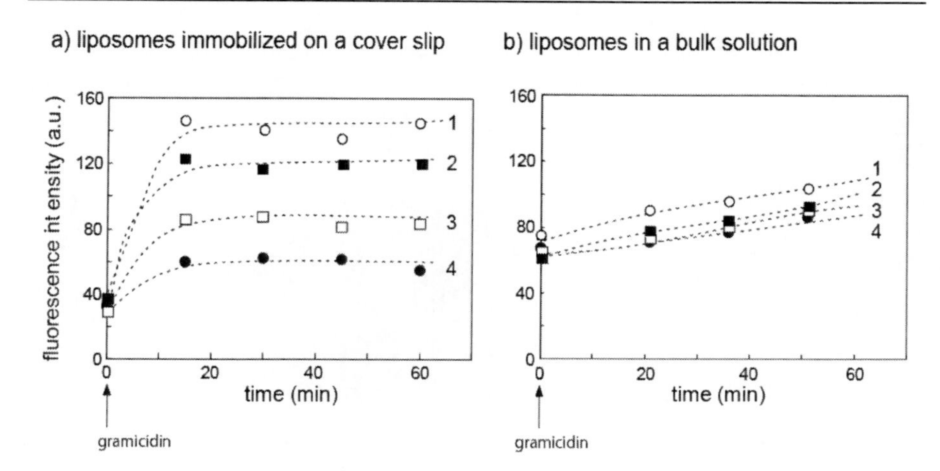

Figure 5. Comparison of time courses of fluorescence intensities from liposomes immobilized on a cover slip (a) and that in a bulk solution (b). Gramicidin concentrations: 1.0 μg/mL. Neurokinin A concentration (g/mL): (1) 10^{-6}, (2) 10^{-7}, (3) 10^{-8} and (4) 10^{-9}.

Simultaneous Quantification of Biomolecules with a Liposome Array

A gramicidin-aided liposome array enables us to quantify multiple biomolecules simultaneously. We applied a liposome array to simultaneous quantification of a family of neuropeptides known as tachykinins, i.e., neurokinin A and substance P(SP). Both molecules in a mixture, both ranging from 0.5×10^{-8} g/mL to 0.5×10^{-6} g/mL, can be quantified with a liposome array [45]. Another example of simultaneous immunoassay with a liposome array is that of somatostatin and growth hormone releasing factor (GHRF). GHRF stimulates secretion of growth hormone (GH) from anterior pituitary gland, which plays role in somatic growth and metabolism [62-64], and somatostatin inhibits the release of GH [65]. The concentration dependence for GHRF and somatostatin with a liposome array is shown in Fig. 6. The Fab' fragment of anti-GHRF was immobilized on column 2 and that of anti-somatostatin was on column 3. The mixture of GHRF and somatostatin in various mixing ratios was applied to the array. As shown in Fig. 6, fluorescence on column 2 increased from the left spot to the right one, corresponding to the increase in the fraction of GHRF in the mixture, whereas fluorescence on column 3 decreased from the left spot to the right one, corresponding to the decrease in the fraction of somatostatin. On the other hand, no noticeable changes in fluorescence intensity were observed on control column 1, where antibody Fab' fragments were absent. The detection limits were 2×10^{-10} g/mL for GHRF and 3×10^{-10} g/mL for somatostatin.

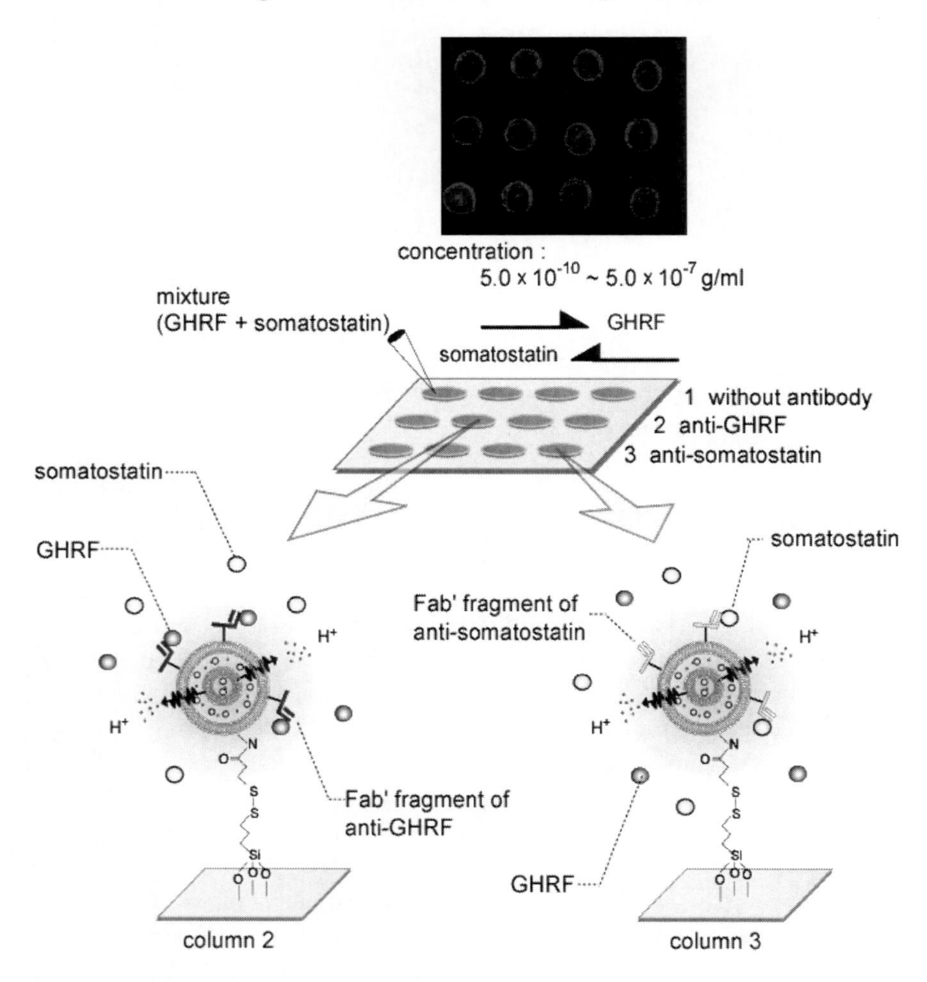

Figure 6. Schematic illustration for simultaneous quantification of GHRF and somatostatin in a mixture with a liposome array. Fluorescence image (ex.488 nm; em. 530 nm).

IMPROVEMENT OF DETECTION LIMITS

The detection limit of liposome arrays described above is typically sub-pg/ml. On the other hand, there exist extremely low levels (fg/ml level) of biomolecules in biological fluids. To improve the detection limit of liposome arrays, we combined the gramicidin-aided immunoassay with immuno-precipitation techniques for enriching analytes [47]. Schematic illustration for the working principle is shown in Fig. 7. Cover slips (24 × 24 mm) are modified with antibody using the conventional immobilization technique.

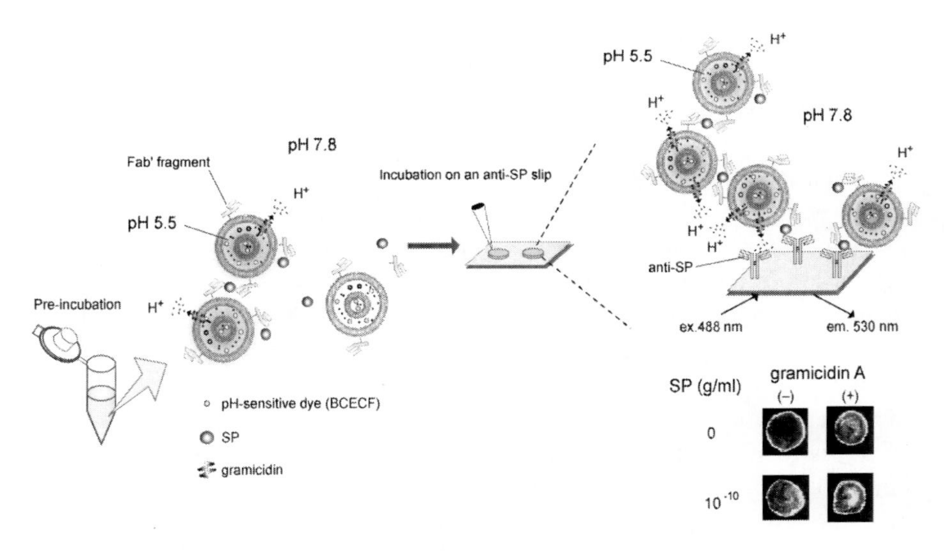

Figure 7. Schematic illustration for the working principle of a gramicidin-aided immunoassay in combination with immuno-precipitation techniques and fluorescence images in the presence and absence of gramicidin (ex.488 nm; em. 530 nm).

On the other hand, a mixture of antigen, gramicidin A and Fab'(anti-analyte)-liposome encapsulating BCECF is pre-incubated in an outer solution of pH 7.8. During pre-incubation time, some fraction of Fab'(anti-analyte)-liposomes is agglutinated and gramicidin is spontaneously incorporated in liposomal lipid bilayers. By spotting a given volume of the mixture on an antibody(not fragment)-modified cover slip, the analyte-bound, agglutinated liposomes are captured on the slip. Based on this technique, we investigated the concentration dependence for SP in a phosphate buffer solution. The fluorescence intensity was plotted against SP concentration in the range from 1.0×10^{-13} to 1.0×10^{-10} g/ml on a linear scale and a logarithmic scale. The lower detection limit for SP was 0.32 pg/ml. The lower detection limit is comparable to that (0.25 pg/ml) of the competitive fluorometric immunoassay [66], but it was much superior to those of the liposome array method (sub-pg/ml) [45], as well as the radioimmunoassay (10–20 pg/ml) [67,68] and the solid-phase immobilized epitope immunoassay (6 pg/ml) [69]. Thus, the combination of gramicidin-aided immunoassay with agglutination/ precipitation techniques could improve the detection-limit of the gramicidin-aided immunoassay.

APPLICATION OF LIPOSOME ARRAYS

Assay Procedure

Human serum was diluted 125 times with a PB solution; 10 μL of serum is mixed with 1.24 mL of a PB solution. For the case of SLO quantification, a known amount of SLO in a PB solution is spiked into the diluted serum. A 5-μL portion of the diluted serum sample is taken and mixed with 5.0 μL of 30 μg/ml gramicidin and 10 μL of 5.4 mg/ml Fab'(anti-SP)-liposome or Fab'(anti-SLO)-liposome. After incubation for 15 min under darkness at room temperature, the mixture is spotted on an anti-SP slip or an anti-SLO slip, and incubated again for 15 min. The spot is washed three times with a PB solution. Then, the slip is subjected to fluorometric image measurements (ex. 488 nm, em. 530 nm). The determination of SP and SLO amounts in serum are based on calibration curves prepared using a known concentration of each compound in a PB solution.

Assay of Substance P in Human Serum

The accurate measurements of SP levels in biological fluids are important for monitoring of various characteristics of health or disease and infection because SP levels are changed by various disease states such as inflammatory disease [70,71], infection disease [72], Alzheimer's disease [73], Parkinson's disease [74] and Huntington's disease [75]. A considerable variation in levels of SP has been reported so far with or without extraction steps. The extraction procedure is likely to eliminate SP bound to proteins with high-molecular (> 400000 Da) and intermediate-molecular (58000 Da) mass nonspecifically [76-78] and leads to underestimates of the total SP amount. On the other hand, dilution of serum or plasma samples increases the ratio of the probe antibody to serum or plasma proteins, allowing effective dissociation of nonspecifically bound to SP from proteins [77,78]. Therefore, immunoassays without extraction steps are preferable for measurements of SP levels in serum or plasma. The gramicidin-aided liposome immunoassay in combination with immune-precipitation is a highly sensitive and rapid method. In this method, 10 mg/ml human serum albumin (HSA) and 0.5 mg/ml γ-globulin did not affect the assay of SP [47]. The method allows determination of SP in 50-125 times diluted human serum. With 125-times dilution, SP amount in 100% human serum (type AB, male, H4522-20ML, Sigma) was obtained as $(2.2 \pm 0.6) \times 10^2$ pg/ml. The SP level in human serum is in agreement with the result obtained with a competitive EIA kit (Cayman EIA kit) and within the range of the reported SP levels in human serum [79-81].

Assay of Streptolysin O in Human Serum

Streptolysin O is a family of the cholesterol-dependent cytolysins (CDCs) secreted by *Streptococcus pyogenes* and causes disruption and lysis of target cell [82]. In general, anti-streptolysin O (ASO), which presents in the serum of a patient with a beta-hemolytic streptococcal infections, is measured for diagnosing streptococcal infections, such as rheumatic fever and glomerulonephritis [83-88]. Quantifying SLO rather than ASO may help us to know an earlier stage of the infections, where the production of ASO is not yet sufficient for detection with ELISA methods. We investigated the quantification of spiked SLO in diluted human serum with a Fab'(anti-SLO)-liposome array. A detection limit of 8 fg/ml was obtained, which is superior to that for SP. This is ascribable to the large-molecular weight of SLO, which may lead to a larger modulation of gramicidin kinetics. The dynamic range of our method is $5.8 \times 10^{-7} - 5.8 \times 10^{-6}$ HU, which is much superior to the electrochemical method (5 -45 HU) [89].

Comparison of Liposome-Based Immuno-Sensing Methods

The strip-based liposome immunoassays, which are relied on detecting intact liposomes, is often used for point of care diagnosis due to simple, rapid and low cost instrument. In many strip-based liposome immunoassays, detection of biomolecules is completed within 30 min, as given in Table 1. However, their detection limits, ranging from ng/ml level to μg/ml level, are not enough to detect low levels of biomolecules, expect for detecting toxins such as cholera toxin and botulinum toxin. Ganglioside (GM1) is spontaneously inserted into lipid bilayers of liposomes and utilized instead of anti-body, enabling detecting toxins with high sensitivity due to strong binding of GM1 to toxins [3,4,6,7,9]. On the other hand, liposome lysis immunoassays allow quantification of biomolecules with higher sensitivity than strip-based liposome immunoassays. The liposome lysis immunoassays based on detecting electroactive molecules, such as potassium ferrocyanide, ferrocene carboxylic acid and a Ru complex, are sensitive methods with detection limits being pg/ml levels [17, 26, 28]. Recently, electrodes modified by nanomaterials, such as carbon nanotube [23], gold nanoparticles [25], nanopore gold [21] have attracted attention for liposome lysis immunoassay because of high sensitivity attributable to a large surface area and enhanced electrocatalytic activity. Liposome immunoassay combined with DNA aptamer-based rolling circle amplification (liposome-RCA assay) has also been reported, as a strategy for attaining high sensitivity of assays, [92-94]. This method enables to detect prostate-specific antigen (PSA) with a detection limit of 0.08 fg/ml [94]. A sandwich format is adapted for many liposome lysis immunoassays. Therefore, the assays tend to be time-consuming. On the other hand, liposome-based flow injection immunoassay [39,40] can be performed within 16-40 min for one sample, but the sensitivity tends to be poor in comparison with liposome-RCA assay.

Our approach for direct immunoassay based on modulation of kinetics of a gramicidin channel in a lipid bilayer has a signal amplification system, which is based on translocation of numerous H^+ ions. In this method, fluorescence emission from liposomes is measured and the method has a lower detection limit which is comparable with those of liposome lysis immunoassay based on detecting electroactive molecules. Further, the assay time is almost the same as that of flow injection liposome immunoassay in a sandwich format. Therefore, the present liposome immunoassay will be a powerful tool for detecting biomolecules rapidly and sensitively, suggesting the potential for applying it to point of care diagnosis.

Table 1. Comparison of liposome immunoassays

analyte	assay format	signal marker	detection limit	assay time	ref.
a) Strip-based liposome assay					
biotin	competitive	SRB	6 ng/ml	–	2
cholera toxin	sandwich	SRB	10 fg/ml	–	3
botulinum toxin	sandwich	SRB	15 pg/ml	20 min	4
cholera toxin	sandwich	SRB	80 fg/ml 3 pg/ml	20 min	6
salmonella	sandwich	MB	10^5 cells/ml	90 min	7
IgE	competitive	SRB	18.5 ng/ml	5 min	8
salmonella	sandwich	SRB	10^2 CFU/ml	25 min	9
b) SPR					
INF-γ	–		1 ng/ml	4 h	90
c) QCM					
cholera toxin	–		1.0×10^{-13} M	–	91
d) Liposome lysis assay					
Ferritin	homogeneous	CF			10
cholera toxin B	sandwich	SRB	340 pg/ml	3.5 h	11
enrofloxacin	homogeneous	SRB	1 ng/g	25 min	12
α-thrombin	sandwich	SRB	2.35 ng/ml	4.5 h	13
cholera toxin	sandwich	potassium ferrocyanide	1 fg/ml	65 min ~	23
PSA	sandwich	ascorbic acid 2-phosphate	7 pg/ml	2 h ~	17
NT-proBNP	sandwich	Cocain, $[Ru(bpy)_3]^{2+}$	0.77 pg/ml	2.5 h ~	28
Mucin-16	sandwich	ferrocen carboxylic acid	5×10^{-4} U/ml	1 h ~	25
cancer antigen 15-3	sandwich	HRP	5×10^{-6} U/ml	1 h ~	21
e) Liposome RCA immunoassay (secondary amplification)					
PSA	sandwich	DNA aptamer	0.08 fg/ml	5.5 h ~	94
f) Combination of Liposome lysis and flow injection analysis					
theophylline	sandwich	CF	<29 nmol/ml	16 min	39
cholera toxin	sandwich	SRB	66 ag/ml	~ 40 min	40
g) Gramicidin-aided immunoassay					
GHRF	array	BCECF	200 pg/ml	~ 40 min	46
somatostatin	array	BCECF	300 pg/ml	~ 40 min	46
substance P	array	BCECF	0.32 pg/ml	~ 1 h	47
streptolysin O	array	BCECF	8 fg/ml	~ 1 h	47

SRB: sulforhodamine B, CF: carboxy fluorescein,

Conclusion and Prospects

The direct immunoassay based on modulation of kinetics of a gramicidin channel in a lipid bilayer measures changes in the physical and chemical properties of lipid bilayers caused by antigen-antibody immunoreaction at the bilayer interface. Liposomes arrayed on a substrate enable us to design a comprehensive and simultaneous analysis system. The principle of the signal amplification can be applied to a variety of immunoassay systems because antibody conjugated to liposomes surface is independent from gramicidin channels. Further, immunoassay based on this amplification principle is highly sensitivity, simple and rapid. The comprehensive and simultaneous analysis technology for biomolecules is important for understanding physiological and pathophysiological phenomena in living cells. For this purpose, high sensitivity is often needed for detecting low levels of biomolecules. An array of liposomes with high sensitivity seems to be useful for comprehensive and simultaneous analyses of biomolecules.

REFERENCES

[1] Bangham A. D. (1968) Membrane models with phospholipids. *Prog. Biophys. Mol. Biol.* 18; 29-95.

[2] Martorell D., Siebert S. T. & Durst R. A. (1999). Liposome dehydration on nitrocellulose and its application in a biotin immunoassay. *Anal. Biochem.* 271(2); 177-185.

[3] Ahn-Yoon S, DeCory T. R., Baeumner A. J., Durst R. A. (2003). Ganglioside-liposome immunoassay for the ultrasensitive detection of cholera toxin. *Anal Chem.* 75(10); 2256-2261.

[4] Ahn-Yoon S, DeCory T. R & Durst R. A. (2004). Ganglioside-liposome immunoassay for the detection of botulinum toxin. (2004). *Anal. Bioanal. Chem.* 378(1); 68-75.

[5] Wen H. W., Borejsza-Wysocki W., DeCory T. R & Durst R. A. (2005). Development of a competitive liposome-based lateral flow assay for the rapid detection of the allergenic peanut protein Ara h1. *Anal. Bioanal. Chem.* 382(5); 1217-1226.

[6] Ahn S & Durst R. A. (2008) Detection of cholera toxin in seafood using a ganglioside-liposome immunoassay. *Anal. Bioanal. Chem.* 391(2); 473-478.

[7] Ho J. A., Zeng S. C., Tseng W. H., Lin Y. J. & Chen C. H. (2008) Liposome-based immunostrip for the rapid detection of Salmonella. *Anal. Bioanal. Chem.* 391(2); 479-485.

[8] Annie Ho J. A., Wu L. C., Chang L. H., Hwang K. C. & Reuben Hwu J. R. (2009) Liposome-based immunoaffinity chromatographic assay for the quantitation of immunoglobulin E in human serum. *J. Chromatogr B.* 878(2); 172-176.

[9] Shukla S., Leem H. & Kim M. (2011). Development of a liposome-based immunochromatographic strip assay for the detection of Salmonella. *Anal. Bioanal. Chem.* 401(8); 2581-2590.

[10] Ishimori Y. & Rokugawa K. (1993). Stable liposomes for assays of human sera. *Clin. Chem.* 39(7); 1439-1443.

[11] Edwards K. A. & March J. C. (2007). GM(1)-functionalized liposomes in a microtiter plate assay for cholera toxin in Vibrio cholerae culture samples. *Anal Biochem.* 368(1); 39-48.

[12] Zhang S., Liu Z., Zhou N., Wang Z. & Shen J. (2008). A liposome immune lysis assay for enrofloxacin in carp and chicken muscle. *Anal. Chim. Acta.* 612(1); 83-88.

[13] Edwards K. A., Wang Y. & Baeumner A. J. (2010). Aptamer sandwich assays: human α-thrombin detection using liposome enhancement. *Anal. Bioanal. Chem.* 398(6); 2645-2654.

[14] Edwards K. A., Meyers K. J., Leonard B. & Baeumner A. J. (2013). Superior performance of liposomes over enzymatic amplification in a high-throughput assay for myoglobin in human serum. *Anal. Bioanal. Chem.* 405(12); 4017-4026.

[15] Vamvakaki V. & Chaniotakis N. A. (2007). Pesticide detection with a liposome-based nano-biosensor. *Biosens Bioelectron.* 22(12); 2848-2853.

[16] Valdés-Ramírez G., Cortina M., Ramírez-Silva M. T. & Marty JL. (2008). Acetylcholinesterase-based biosensors for quantification of carbofuran, carbaryl, methylparaoxon, and dichlorvos in 5% acetonitrile. *Anal. Bioanal. Chem.* 392(4); 699-707.

[17] Qu B., Guo L., Chu X., Wu D. H., Shen G. L. & Yu R. Q. (2010). An electrochemical immunosensor based on enzyme-encapsulated liposomes and biocatalytic metal deposition. *Anal. Chim. Acta.* 663(2); 147-152.

[18] Yoshimoto M., Iida C., Kariya A., Takaki N., Nakayama M. (2010). A Biosensor Composed of Glucose Oxidase-Containing Liposomes and MnO2-Based Layered Nanocomposite. *Electroanalysis* 22(6); 653-659.

[19] Di Tuoro D., Portaccio M., Lepore M., Arduini F., Moscone D., Bencivenga U. & Mita D. G.. (2011). An acetylcholinesterase biosensor for determination of low concentrations of Paraoxon and Dichlorvos. *N. Biotechnol.* 29(1); 132-138.

[20] Hsin T. M., Wu K. & Chellappan G.. (2012). Magnetically immobilized nanoporous giant proteoliposomes as a platform for biosensing. *Analyst*, 137(1); 245-248.

[21] Ge S., Jiao X. & Chen D. (2012). Ultrasensitive electrochemical immunosensor for CA 15-3 using thionine-nanoporous gold-graphene as a platform and horseradish peroxidase-encapsulated liposomes as signal amplification. *Analyst.* 137(19); 4440-4447.

[22] Sasaki Y., Shioyama Y., Tian W. J., Kikuchi J., Hiyama S., Moritani Y & Suda T. (2010). A nanosensory device fabricated on a liposome for detection of chemical signals. *Biotechnol Bioeng.* 105(1); 37-43.

[23] Viswanathan S., Wu L. C., Huang M. R. & Ho J. A. (2006). Electrochemical immunosensor for cholera toxin using liposomes and poly(3,4-ethylenedioxythiophene)-coated carbon nanotubes. *Anal Chem.* 78(4); 1115-1121.

[24] Viswanathan S., Rani C., Vijay Anand A. & Ho J. A. (2009) Disposable electrochemical immunosensor for carcinoembryonic antigen using ferrocene liposomes and MWCNT screen-printed electrode. *Biosens. Bioelectron.* 24(7); 1984-1989.

[25] Viswanathan S., Rani C. & Delerue-Matos C. (2012). Ultrasensitive detection of ovarian cancer marker using immunoliposomes and gold nanoelectrodes. *Anal. Chim. Acta.* 726; 79-84.

[26] Egashira N., Morita S., Hifumi E., Mitoma Y. & Uda T. (2008). Attomole detection of hemagglutinin molecule of influenza virus by combining an electrochemiluminescence sensor with an immunoliposome that encapsulates a Ru complex. (2008). *Anal. Chem.* 80(11); 4020-4025.

[27] Zhan W. & Bard A. J. (2007). Electrogenerated chemiluminescence. 83. Immunoassay of human C-reactive protein by using Ru(bpy)3(2+)-encapsulated liposomes as labels. *Anal Chem.* 79(2); 459-463.

[28] Mao L., Yuan R., Chai Y., Zhuo Y. & Xiang Y. (2011). Signal-enhancer molecules encapsulated liposome as a valuable sensing and amplification platform combining the aptasensor for ultrasensitive ECL immunoassay. *Biosens. Bioelectron.* 26(10); 4204-4208.

[29] Edwards K. A. & Baeumner A. J. (2006). Liposomes in analyses (Review). *Talanta* 68(5); 1421-1431.

[30] Edwards K. A., Bolduc O. R. & Baeumner A. J. (2012). Miniaturized bioanalytical systems: enhanced performance through liposomes (Review). *Curr. Opin. Chem. Biol.* 16(3-4); 444-452.

[31] Liu Q & Boyd BJ. (2013). Liposomes in biosensors (Review). *Analyst* 138(2); 391-409.

[32] Lim S. J, & Kim C. K. (1997). Homogeneous liposome immunoassay for insulin using phospholipase C from Clostridium perfringens. *Anal. Biochem.* 247(1); 89-95.

[33] Liu D. & Huang L. (1992). Trypsin-induced lysis of lipid vesicles: effect of surface charge and lipid composition. *Anal. Biochem.* 202(1); 1-5.

[34] Tomioka K., Kii F., Fukuda H. & Katoh S. (1994). Homogeneous immunoassay of antibody by use of liposomes made of a model lipid of archaebacteria. *J. Immunol. Methods.* 176(1); 1-7.

[35] Ho R. J. & Huang L. (1985). Interactions of antigen-sensitized liposomes with immobilized antibody: a homogeneous solid-phase immunoliposome assay. *J. Immunol.* 134(6); 4035-4040.

[36] Kim C. K. & Park K. M. (1994). Liposome immunoassay (LIA) for gentamicin using phospholipase C. *J. Immunol. Methods.* 170(2); 225-31.

[37] Locascio-Brown L., Plant A. L. & Durst R. A. (1988). Behavior of liposomes in flow injection systems. Anal. Chem. 60(8); 792-797.

[38] Plant A. L. (1986). Mechanism of concentration quenching of a xanthene dye encapsulated in phospholipid vesicles. *Photochem. Photobiol.* 44(4); 453-459.

[39] Locascio-Brown L., Plant A. L., Chesler R., Kroll M., Ruddel M. & Durst RA. (1993). Liposome-based flow-injection immunoassay for determining theophylline in serum. *Clin Chem.* 39(3); 386-391.

[40] Ho J. A., Wu L. C., Huang M. R., Lin Y. J., Baeumner A. J. & Durst R. A. (2007). Application of ganglioside-sensitized liposomes in a flow injection immunoanalytical system for the determination of cholera toxin. *Anal. Chem.* 279(1); 246-250.

[41] Kolusheva S., Kafri R., Katz M. & Jelinek R. (2001). Rapid colorimetric detection of antibody-epitope recognition at a biomimetic membrane interface. *J. Am. Chem. Soc.* 123(3); 417-422.

[42] Yuan Z. & Hanks W. T. (2006). A reversible colorimetric and fluorescent polydiacetylene vesicle sensor platform. *Polymer* 49(23); 5023-5026.

[43] Jung Y. K., Park H. G. & Kim J. M. (2006). Polydiacetylene (PDA)-based colorimetric detection of biotin-streptavidin interactions. *Biosens. Bioelectron.* 21(8); 1536-1544.

[44] Xia Y., Deng J. & Jiang L. (2010). Simple and highly sensitive detection of hepatotoxin microcystin-LR via colorimetric variation based on polydiacetylene vesicles. Sens. Actuators B Chem. 145(2); 713-719.

[45] Horie M., Yanagisawa H. & Sugawara M. (2007). Fluorometric immunoassay based on pH-sensitive dye-encapsulating liposomes and gramicidin channels. *Anal. Biochem.* 369(2); 192-201.

[46] Shoji A., Sugimoto E., Orita S., Nozawa K., Yanagida A., Shibusawa Y. & Sugawara M. (2010). A reusable liposome array and its application to assay of growth-hormone-related peptides. *Anal. Bioanal. Chem.* 397(3); 1377-1381.

[47] Sakamoto M., Shoji A. & Sugawara M. (2013). Highly Sensitive and Rapid Assay of Substance P and Streptolysin O in Human Serum Using Immuno-liposomes and Gramicidin Channels. *Anal. Sci.* 29(9); 877-883.

[48] Gonzalez L. C. (2012). Protein microarrays, biosensors, and cell-based methods for secretome-wide extracellular protein-protein interaction mapping (Review). *Methods.* 57(4);448-458.

[49] Usui K, Tomizaki K. & Mihara H. (2009). A designed peptide chip: protein fingerprinting technology with a dry peptide array and statistical data mining (Review). *Methods Mol. Biol.* 570; 273-284.

[50] Cosnier S. & Mailley P. (2008). Recent advances in DNA sensors (Review). *Analyst.* 133(8), 984-991.

[51] de Planell-Saguer M. & Rodicio M. C. (2011). Analytical aspects of microRNA in diagnostics: a review (Review). *Anal Chim Acta.* 699(2); 134-152.

[52] Yang Q., Liu X. Y., Yoshimoto M., Kuboi R. & Miyake J. (1999). Covalent immobilization of unilamellar liposomes in gel beads for chromatography. *Anal. Biochem.* 268(2); 354-362.

[53] Wang S., Yoshimoto M., Fukunaga K. & Nakao K. (2003). Optimal covalent immobilization of glucose oxidase-containing liposomes for highly stable biocatalyst in bioreactor. *Biotechnol. Bioeng.* 83(4); 444-453.

[54] Morita S., Nukui M. & Kuboi R. (2006). Immobilization of liposomes onto quartz crystal microbalance to detect interaction between liposomes and proteins. *J. Colloid Interface Sci.* 298(2); 672-678.

[55] Yang Q., Liu X. Y., Umetani K., Kamo N. & Miyake J. (1999). Partitioning of triphenylalkylphosphonium homologues in gel bead-immobilized liposomes: chromatographic measurement of their membrane partition coefficients. *Biochim. Biophys. Acta.* 1417(1); 122-130.

[56] Losey E. A., Smith M. D., Meng M. & Best M. D. (2009). Microplate-based analysis of protein-membrane binding interactions via

immobilization of whole liposomes containing a biotinylated anchor. *Bioconjug Chem.* 0(2); 376-383.

[57] Ornskov E., Ullsten S., Söderberg L., Markides K. E. & Folestad S. Method for immobilization of liposomes in capillary electrophoresis by electrostatic interaction with derivatized agarose. *Electrophoresis.* 23(19); 3381-3384.

[58] Zhang L., Hong L., Yu Y., Bae S. C. & Granick S. (2006). Nanoparticle-assisted surface immobilization of phospholipid liposomes. *J. Am. Chem. Soc.* 128(28); 9026-9027.

[59] Yoshina-Ishii C., Miller G. P., Kraft M. L., Kool E. T. & Boxer S. G. (2006). General method for modification of liposomes for encoded assembly on supported bilayers. *J. Am. Chem. Soc.* 127(5); 1356-1357.

[60] Yoshina-Ishii C. & Boxer S. G.. (2006). Controlling two-dimensional tethered vesicle motion using an electric field: interplay of electrophoresis and electro-osmosis. *Langmuir.* 22(5); 2384-2391.

[61] Lundbaek J. A., Collingwood S. A., Ingólfsson H. I., Kapoor R. & Andersen O. S. (2010). Lipid bilayer regulation of membrane protein function: gramicidin channels as molecular force probes. *J. R. Soc. Interface.* 7(44); 373-395.

[62] Flint D. J, Binart N., Kopchick J. & Kelly P. (2003). Effects of growth hormone and prolactin on adipose tissue development and function (Review). *Pituitary* 6(2); 97-102.

[63] Giustina A., & Veldhuis J. D. (1998). Pathophysiology of the neuroregulation of growth hormone secretion in experimental animals and the human (Review). *Endocr Rev* 19(6); 717-797.

[64] Ikeda A., Chang K. T., Matsumoto Y., Furuhata Y., Nishihara M., Sasaki F. & Takahashi M. (1998). Obesity and insulin resistance in human growth hormone transgenic rats (Review). *Endocrinology* 139(7); 3057-3063.

[65] Müller E. E., Locatelli V. & Cocchi D. (1999). Neuroendocrine control of growth hormone secretion (Review). *Physiol Rev* 79(2); 511-607.

[66] Suzuki Y., Itoh H., Abe T., Nishimura F., Sato Y. & Takeyama M. (2011). Comparison of the effects of pantethine and fursultiamine on plasma gastrointestinal peptide levels in healthy volunteers. *Biol. Pharm. Bull.* 34(10); 1640-1643.

[67] Nemmar A., Gustin P., Delaunois A., Beckers J. F & Sulon J. (1998). Radioimmunoassay of substance P in lung perfusate. *J. Pharmacol. Toxicol. Methods.* 39(2); 109-115.

[68] Lambiase A., Bonini S., Micera A., Tirassa P., Magrini L., Bonini S. & Aloe L. (1997). increased plasma levels of substance P in vernal keratoconjunctivitis. *Invest. Ophthalmol. Vis. Sci.* 38(10); 2161-2164

[69] Pradelles P., Grassi J., Créminon C., Boutten B. & Mamas S. (1994). immunometric assay of low molecular weight haptens containing primary amino groups. *Anal. Chem.* 66(1); 16-22.

[70] Garrett N. E., Mapp P. I., Cruwys S. C., Kidd B. L. & Blake D. R. (1992). Role of substance P in inflammatory arthritis. *Ann. Rheum. Dis.* 51(8); 1014-1018.

[71] Keeble J. E & Brain S. D. A role for substance P in arthritis? *Neurosci. Lett.* 361(1-3); 176-179.

[72] Holzer P. (1998). Implications of tachykinins and calcitonin gene-related peptide in inflammatory bowel disease. *Digestion.* 59(4):269-283.

[73] Bouras C., Vallet P. G., Hof P. R., Charnay Y., Golaz J. & Constantinidis J. (1990). Substance P immunoreactivity in Alzheimer disease: a study in cases presenting symmetric or asymmetric cortical atrophy. *Alzheimer Dis. Assoc. Disord.* 4(1):24-34.

[74] Gresch P. J. & Walker P. D. (1999). Serotonin-2 receptor stimulation normalizes striatal preprotachykinin messenger RNA in an animal model of Parkinson's disease. *Neuroscience.* 93(3); 831-841.

[75] Buck S. H., Burks T. F., Brown M. R. & Yamamura H. I. (1981). Reduction in basal ganglia and substantia nigra substance P levels in Huntington's disease. *Brain Res.* 209(2):464-469.

[76] Corbally N., Powell D. & Tipton K. F. (1990). The binding of endogenous and exogenous substance-P in human plasma. *Biochem. Pharmacol.* 39(7); 1161-1166.

[77] Campbell D. E, Raftery N., Tustin R. 3rd, Tustin N. B., Desilvio M. L., Cnaan A., Aye P. P., Lackner A. A. & Douglas S. D. (2006). Measurement of plasma-derived substance P: biological, methodological, and statistical considerations. *Clin. Vaccine. Immunol.* 13(11); 1197-1203.

[78] Campbell D. E., Bruckner P., Tustin N. B., Tustin R 3rd & Douglas S. D. (2009). Novel method for determination of substance P levels in unextracted human plasma by using acidification. *Clin. Vaccine. Immunol.* 16(4); 594-596.

[79] Kunt T., Forst T., Schmidt S., Pfützner A., Schneider S., Harzer O., Löbig M., Engelbach M., Goitom K., Pohlmann T. & Beyer J. (2000). Serum levels of substance P are decreased in patients with type 1 diabetes. *Exp. Clin. Endocrinol. Diabetes.* 108(3); 164-167.

[80] Bondy B., Baghai T. C., Minov C., Schüle C., Schwarz M. J., Zwanzger P., Rupprecht R. & Möller H. J. (2003). Substance P serum levels are increased in major depression: preliminary results. *Biol. Psychiatry.* 53(6); 538-542.

[81] Grimsholm O., Rantapää-Dahlqvist S. & Forsgren S. (2005). Levels of gastrin-releasing peptide and substance P in synovial fluid and serum correlate with levels of cytokines in rheumatoid arthritis. *Arthritis. Res. Ther.* 7(3); R416-R426.

[82] Todd E. W. (1932). Antigenic Streptococcal Hemolysin. *J. Exp. Med.* 55(2); 267-280.

[83] Ben-Chetrit E., Moses A. E., Agmon-Levin N., Block C. & Ben-Chetrit E. (2012). Serum levels of anti-streptolysin O antibodies: their role in evaluating rheumatic diseases. *Int. J. Rheum. Dis.* 15(1); 78-85.

[84] Gerber M. A., Caparas L. S. & Randolph M. F. (1990). Evaluation of a new latex agglutination test for detection of streptolysin O antibodies. *J. Clin. Microbiol.* 28(3); 413-415.

[85] Kubotsu K., Ushio I., Yoshikawa K., Kida M., Ishikawa K., Matsuura S. & Sakurabayashi I. (1990). Colorimetric liposome lysis for assay of anti-streptolysin O antibody. *Clin. Chem.* 36(10); 1747-1749.

[86] Umeda M., Tomita T., Shibata H., Seki M. & Yasuda T. (1988). Homogeneous liposome lysis assay for determination of anti-streptolysin O antibody titer in serum. *J. Clin. Microbiol.* 26(5); 804-807.

[87] Heath-Fracica L. A. & Estévez EG. (1987). Evaluation of a new latex agglutination test for detection of streptococcal antibodies. *Diagn. Microbiol. Infect. Dis.* 8(1); 25-30.

[88] Kodama T., Ichiyama S., Morishita Y., Fukatsu T., Shimokata K. & Nakashima N. (1997). Determination of anti-streptolysin O antibody titer by a new passive agglutination method using sensitized toraysphere particles. *J. Clin. Microbiol.* 35(4); 839-842.

[89] Xu D. & Cheng Q. (2002). Surface-bound lipid vesicles encapsulating redox species for amperometric biosensing of pore-forming bacterial toxins. *J. Am. Chem. Soc.* 124(48); 14314-14315.

[90] Wink T., van Zuilen S. J., Bult A. & van Bennekom W. P. (1998). Liposome-mediated enhancement of the sensitivity in immunoassays of proteins and peptides in surface plasmon resonance spectrometry. *Anal. Chem.* 70(5); 827-832.

[91] Alfonta L., Willner I., Throckmorton D. J. & Singh A. K. (2001). Electrochemical and quartz crystal microbalance detection of the cholera

toxin employing horseradish peroxidase and GM1-functionalized liposomes. *Anal. Chem.* 73(21); 5287-5295.

[92] Zhou L.,, Ou L. J., Chu X., Shen G. L. & Yu R. Q. (2007). Aptamer-based rolling circle amplification: a platform for electrochemical detection of protein. *Anal. Chem.* 79(19); 7492-7500.

[93] Edwards K. A. & Baeumner A. J. (2007). DNA-oligonucleotide encapsulating liposomes as a secondary signal amplification means. *Anal. Chem.* 79(5); 1806-1815.

[94] Ou L. J., Liu S. J., Chu X., Shen G. L. & Yu R. Q. (2009). DNA encapsulating liposome based rolling circle amplification immunoassay as a versatile platform for ultrasensitive detection of protein. *Anal. Chem.* 81(23); 9664-9673.

INDEX

A

B

C

D

E

F

G

H

I

K

L

T

U

V